YOGA PRESCRIBED

Love, light +
blessings,
Carole x

An environmentally friendly book. Contents printed on 100% recycled, unbleached paper, from post-consumer waste.

Printed and bound in England.

Also by Carole Kerton:

WHY AM I HERE THIS TIME? MEMOIRS OF A YOGA TEACHER

Available online from Amazon and The Fast-Print Bookshop

YOGA PRESCRIBED

Carole Kerton

MARVELLOUS BOOKS

Published by

MARVELLOUS BOOKS
24 Kemplay Road, London NW3 1SY
info@marvellousbooks.com
www.marvellousbooks.com

First Edition 2014

Copyright © 2014 by Carole Kerton

All rights reserved. This book or any portion thereof may not be reproduced or used in any manner whatsoever without the express written permission of the publisher and copyright owner, except for the use of brief quotations in a book review or scholarly journal.

All the characters in this book are fictitious. Any similarities to real people is purely coincidental.

ISBN: 978-1-909900-06-6

Printed by Book Printing UK, Remus House, Coltsfoot Drive, Peterborough, PE2 9BF

Dedicated to all those enlightened medical folk
who recommend yoga to their patients.

Acknowledgements

I would like to express my heartfelt thanks to Kristina Howell for her advice and her skills. Kristy believes, like me, that if one person gains from this book the project has been worthwhile.

I would also like to thank my family for their unstinting love and support.

CHAPTER 1

SUSIE AND THE BEST JOB IN THE WORLD

It is that wonderfully nurturing moment, when the yoga students are relaxing at the end of their practice, and the teacher is watching over them. Susie loved this time and delighted in 'visiting' each student, spiritually wrapping them in her love and care. This particular group was a firm favourite. Most of them had been coming for a long time to this Wednesday morning class. There was dear Judith, who had tried yoga as an antidote to severe depression; there was John, who had come with back pain; and there was Lauren, who just needed time out in her hectic life.

Susie had been teaching yoga for fifteen years. She had begun attending classes to address her stress levels. Her very first class was like 'coming home', and she was an immediate convert. Her teacher was one of those people that you feel you know. She was friendly, funny, enthusiastic and yet incredibly knowledgeable. Her classes became a lifeline to Susie, as she gradually found her way back to herself. She attended classes for two years and then began to book for retreats. It was not long before she felt compelled to train as a yoga teacher, and so she was delighted to discover that her teacher was also a tutor, a teacher trainer. What a journey that was! The diploma course gave Susie a huge opportunity to explore the philosophy of yoga, and to begin her life-long search for strength, suppleness, stamina and spirituality.

That morning's practice focussed on being grounded. It was based on the root chakra, one of the seven main wheels of energy. They had worked with lots of strong, standing postures. Folk can begin yoga at any time, simply because everyone works with their own awareness, and there had been a new girl that morning. Her name was Bridget and she was pregnant with her third child. Susie had kept a special eye on her, giving her alternatives to the postures unsuitable for pregnancy. She knew, from experience, that the meditation, breath-work and relaxation would be invaluable for Bridget.

The class came to a close with the familiar 'OM SHANTI SHANTI SHANTI'. *Om* is the universal sound and is a sacred symbol. *Shanti* means 'peace' and is such a crucial message: 'Go in peace'. Everyone gathered up their mats and meditation stools, and Susie locked the hall and walked to her car with her friend and student, Kate. They parted with a hug, before Susie headed off to the supermarket to buy vegetables for the boys' dinner.

Susie and Rob Crawford had twin boys, now aged twelve. Max Jonty was the practical one; he always followed Rob around as a little one, 'fixin fings'. Toby Bryce was of a more artistic and dramatic bent. He was inclined to be a dreamer. Both boys had attended Susie's children's yoga classes, and had enjoyed the companionship of other yogis. Now, though, they had become heavily involved with sports and after-school activities, and their yoga had gone on the back burner.

Susie arrived home with her groceries to be greeted by their cat, Pat. The twins had named the gorgeous little black and white kitten with the Postman Pat programme in mind and although the name was based on a mistake, since Postman Pat's cat was actually called Jess, Pat suited him well. He rubbed around Susie's legs as she deposited the food and picked up a message from the answerphone. It was her mother, who had forgotten that she was teaching that morning and had phoned in order to catch up. She would call back later.

Susie ate some hummus on toast, then went upstairs to tidy the boys' bedrooms. She and Rob had moved into a terraced cottage shortly after they got married. It was tiny and was the middle of three Victorian cottages, which had lovely country views. They were sandwiched between Ted and Alice (on the left as you looked at the row of houses) and Brian and Julie (on the right). Ted and Alice 'adopted' the young couple immediately and delighted in giving them seedlings for their garden, and then later feeding Pat while they were away.

Susie and Rob slowly modernised the cottage, taking their time as money was tight. Fortunately, Rob was a patient soul and had an aptitude for practical tasks. (He was a whizz on the computer and worked as a web designer.) Often, he called in the help of his father, when a project required two workmen. Susie's department was the decorating, and the soft furnishing, which she loved.

It was just before the twins were born that they first noticed the rows coming from Brian and Julie's cottage. There was much slamming of doors, and Julie's eyes were puffy and red when they met her on the path. Susie, lumbering along with her huge pregnant abdomen, did her best to comfort Julie and to offer a 'shoulder to cry on'. She and Brian shared a volatile relationship. He was not a man to compromise. Julie's nature, meanwhile, was gentle, quiet and sensitive. She was somewhat dreamy, much preferring to sit and read a book rather than cook the dinner.

Well, the discord escalated and eventually the couple split up. Julie returned home to her parents for a while and Brian moved in with a friend. They put their cottage on the market and Rob became determined to buy it. Susie could fully embrace the plan. They were certainly fast out-growing their tiny home and, with two babies on the way, the extra space would be essential. She did worry about the finance, though. Already her salary had reduced, as she was on maternity leave. How would they cope with increasing their mortgage hugely? Rob was determined. He pushed the deal through, and they certainly never regretted it. It eventually gave them a beautiful four-bedroomed home, and two of those bedrooms were her destination now.

It always amused Susie to observe how very different her boys were! Max's room was filled with half-completed projects. He had an inventor's mind and was fascinated by architecture. His big dream was to build his own 'eco-friendly house'. Toby's room, on the other hand, was awash with papers. He scribbled down short stories, constantly, and delighted in creating his own comic strips. Susie tidied, straightening up their beds and putting clothes into the laundry basket. Pat followed her from room to room and sat on the window-sills to watch the birds.

Susie counted her blessings on a very regular basis. She knew that she was very fortunate with her life and lifestyle – fortunate that her beloved twins were well and happy; fortunate that her marriage was comfortable and compatible; fortunate that she had a career which was rewarding and which served the community – but Susie was always driven by an underlying feeling of guilt. Her manner was bright and friendly, but sometimes this was a façade. It was a disguise to hide the deep wound which never quite healed.

For a brief moment, she stood by the window and looked out, as Pat was doing, and she allowed herself an indulgent stab of self-pity, a visit with that place within her where she permanently missed her father. Then she gave herself a shake, prayed fervently that her boys would always have their wonderful father close at hand, and went downstairs to prepare the vegetables.

After a noisy dinner, with both boys talking at once, Susie prepared for her evening class. She taught ten classes per week: three on Mondays, two on Tuesdays, Wednesdays and Thursdays, and one on a Friday. Her fifteen years of teaching yoga had created a strong following, and Susie was every bit as enthusiastic now as she had been on her first class as a fresh-faced teacher. It surely was the best job in the world!

Rob and Susie had been invited for lunch on one occasion with local friends, Annie and Charles. It was a rare occasion for them to be out without the boys, and they thoroughly enjoyed themselves. Susie chose her outfit carefully. She was slim, from all her yoga, and quite tiny. Her chestnut-coloured hair had a mind of its own, and she drew up the unruly curls into a ponytail. Her make-up flattered her hazel eyes and high cheekbones. Rob loved the way that she looked and told her that she was particularly beautiful that day. During the pre-lunch chat at Annie's delightful country house, they met a lady doctor, whose practice was based in a cosmopolitan area of London. She explained to them that she kept on her desk a prescription pad of details about the local yoga teacher's classes. Any patient who would obviously benefit from yoga, would be given a slip. She was an enlightened soul, who fully embraced the idea of prevention being better than cure. This was truly 'Yoga Prescribed'.

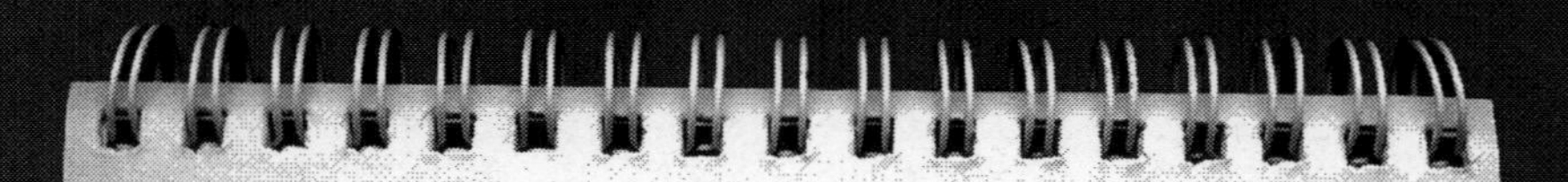

Suggestions from *Yoga Prescribed*

Meditation, breath-work and relaxation are helpful aids during pregnancy.

(All suggestions are based on anecdotal evidence and are in no way a substitute for medical advice.)

CHAPTER 2

TED, ALICE AND THE RED TABLECLOTH

How Susie, Rob and the boys enjoyed living next door to Ted and Alice. They were country folk; Ted had worked with his father as a market gardener, and was a fount of knowledge. He was always pottering out in his greenhouse, in all weathers, and delighted in his vegetable plot, now that he was retired. He loved to share his produce with the young family next door: marrows, courgettes, tomatoes, perpetual spinach and rhubarb. Meanwhile, Alice would be busy making marmalade, jam and the most delicious sponge cakes. Now and then, when the weather was particularly lovely in the summer, they would invite their young neighbours in for afternoon tea. Ted had constructed a small summerhouse, at the end of the garden, and they would lay up the garden table with a jolly red-checked cloth and Alice would cover it with scones, jam, cream, little fancy cakes and big chocolate sponges. Toby and Max were in heaven!

Ted and Alice had a daughter who had emigrated to Australia, and a son who lived in Watford with his partner. To hear them talk, you would have thought that both places were equally distant. They were born, grew up, married and lived in the same village all their lives. They were happy and had no driving desire to travel. They readily opened their hearts to the boys and became adopted grandparents.

Alice had a wealth of knowledge about natural remedies. It was she who told Susie about the town in America where there had been a horrible outbreak of a killer flu. People were actually dying, and the local doctor noticed that one farming family had no members with the illness at all. He made it his business to call by, and to ask the farmer's wife if she was doing anything special as a preventative. She disclosed that she placed a cut onion beside everyone's beds. After three days, she would compost the onion and replace it with a fresh one. The doctor took one such onion for analysis and, sure enough, it contained the flu virus. The raw onion was drawing the germs in to itself, while the family slept! Susie happily shared this information with her students and many immediately implemented it.

Ted looked at Alice's more bizarre superstitions and folklore with a long-suffering and tolerant grin. She always put her left sock on first. This was because she believed that it was bad luck to put your right sock on first on the first of the month. She hedged her bets and trained herself so that could never occur! She also always said, 'White Rabbits' on the first day of the month and no-one quite knew why! She had an answer for all health queries, and she grew herbs in tubs beside the back door, which she used for making teas and bathing solutions. Alice kept tea tree oil upstairs and downstairs, so that it was readily available for any cuts, grazes or fungal infections. Her lavender oil was permanently available, too. It proved so helpful for burns (touching the hot iron, for instance), for insect stings and for sore muscles. Alice had discovered that Susie was very open to all her old-fashioned remedies and, although she had never attended a yoga class, when Susie talked about the yoga philosophy and the fact that it was holistic – working with the whole being – she could fully resonate with its beliefs. They both used flower remedies to ease anxiety and emotional upheaval.

Ted was an old-fashioned gentleman. He was mild of manner, and he liked nothing better than watching his wife and their next-door neighbour deep in conversation. He was the kind of guy who was always around if a neighbour needed a hand, and could often be seen trundling his wheelbarrow up the lane with plants or logs for someone else. Ted was a bell-ringer at the local church, All Saints. He began ringing there as a teenager, and in those days the bell-ringers were the fire brigade also! When they were called to a fire, there was a mass exodus from the bell tower. Ted had risen to the dizzy heights of Tower Captain, and he had a pretty good team of ringers. Their biggest concern was the fact that they were all getting older. Bell-ringing was a dying art. It seemed that young people were not interested to take up this hobby. Ted had his eye firmly set on young Toby and Max, and was biding his time for just the right moment. He had found bell-ringing to be hugely rewarding. It was about community; each bell-ringer watching the circle and concentrating on his neighbour. It was about the wider community, too. After all, the bells called the village in to worship. It takes some physical skill, and some strength, especially when ringing up the tenor, but it is cerebral as well. The methods are quite complex, and ringing a quarter peal, or a full peal, takes concentration and knowledge. The twins were bright enough to pick it up, certainly, and may be tempted by the promise of payment for ringing at weddings. It was such a lovely occasion to be involved in someone's 'big day', and the joyful sound of the bells is integral to the atmosphere.

Alice and Ted remembered the bells ringing at their own wedding back in 1964. Alice had made her own dress, and she and her sister had arranged the flowers in the church. They had their reception in the village hall, and her mother had made the cake. It was beautiful, trimmed with tiny roses. Ted's father had provided all the fruit and vegetables for the wedding breakfast, and his mother had clucked around all day, making sure that everyone had enough to eat. Impossible to believe that they had been married for almost fifty years! It would be their Golden Wedding Anniversary this summer.

Alice still made some of her own clothes and, if she was feeling energetic, would round the outfit off with a matching hat. She liked to embroider and to do needlepoint, but found that her eyes would tire a little more readily than they used to. When the twins were small, she loved to knit for them. She had sent knitted sweaters out to her grandchildren in Australia, until her daughter, Rosemary, had tactfully pointed out that it was too hot to need them. Rosemary had married well. Her husband was a doctor and was called Jonathan. He and Ted were very different characters and, whilst you might imagine that, since they both loved Rosemary they would have at least something in common, this proved not to be the case. Indeed, no-one who knew and understood Ted's kindness and good nature, could believe how adamant he was in his dislike for Jonathan.

Rosemary had gone off to University College London, much to the huge pride of her parents. She was a bright girl, and pretty, and they missed her greatly. In her second year, she met a brash young Australian and fell head over heels in love. Jonathan was training as a doctor and was on a year's secondment to St Bartholomew's. He was handsome, ambitious, materialistic and super determined. His pace was fast; he moved through life at a break-neck speed and had no desire to sit still and chew the fat. It was clear from the very first time that he met Rosemary's parents, that their attitudes to life were juxtaposed. But Rosemary was in love, and nothing was going to stop her marrying her doctor and moving to the other side of the world. Whether she had ever regretted her rashness was a moot point.

Aware of her parents' Golden Wedding Anniversary looming, Rosemary had entered into a series of emails with her brother,

James. They had explored all sorts of ideas. How about renting Lord Byron's cottage for the weekend, and getting all the family together? Or flying Ted and Alice out to Australia? What about treating them to a cruise? All their ideas were lovely but they knew, in their heart of hearts, that their parents would far prefer to rent the village hall and to be surrounded by their local friends and community. They needed to get Susie and Rob on board.

When Susie received Rosemary's email, sounding them out about the anniversary celebrations, she was in the throes of nursing the twins. They had picked up a horrible virus and were coughing all night long. Alice had recommended echinacea. She suggested that the boys should take it for eight days, then have eight days off, and then take it for a further eight days. Echinacea supports and strengthens the immune system. She also recommended steamy bowls with a few drops of lavender oil. It is wonderful for inhalation, and clears blocked nasal passages quickly. The boys had lost their appetites, but Susie insisted that they drank water and kept themselves hydrated. They were downstairs in their pyjamas, looking very sorry for themselves, when Susie picked up the email from Australia on the laptop. 'This might be just the ticket to cheer Toby and Max up,' Susie thought. This proved to be the case, and the lads were soon brainstorming about invitations and entertainment. They loved Ted and Alice dearly, and were over the moon to be involved with their special day.

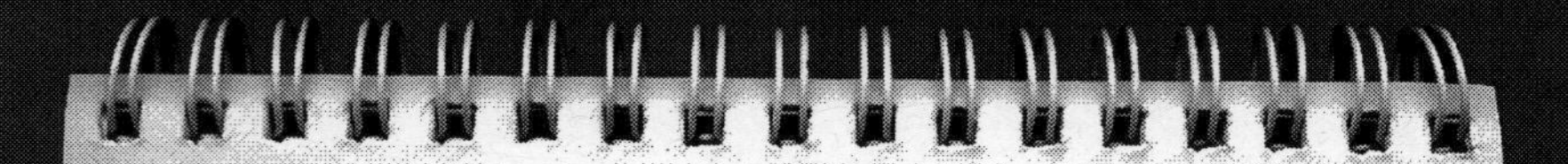

Suggestions from *Yoga Prescribed*

Cutting a raw onion in half and placing it beside the bed at night can help to prevent colds and influenza.

Tea tree oil is helpful for cuts, grazes and fungal infections.

Lavender oil is helpful for burns, insect bites and sore muscles. It can also be used in steamy bowls for clearing blocked nasal passages.

Echinacea is helpful for warding off viruses, coughs and colds. It builds up the immune system. It is apparently best to take it for eight days, and then to have eight days rest from it.

(All suggestions are based on anecdotal evidence and are in no way a substitute for medical advice.)

CHAPTER 3

MARION, JIM AND THE DOLL'S TEA SET

That week, Susie had planned a class on the abdomen and the wheel of energy known as the sacral chakra. This energy centre is concerned with procreation, placed as it is two inches above the base of the spine. It is about creativity, emotions and the joy of being in a body. According to New Age thinking, it is orange in colour, which is also said to be the colour of yoga. Susie was always amused by the giggles from the classes when they reached the balance known as *Merudandasana.* This involved balancing on the sit bones, with ankles held and legs wide. She remembered her yoga teacher saying that, "Enlightenment does not have to be serious!"

In any given week, there would be students who had particular concerns, perhaps health related, or maybe to do with their family. The yoga teacher's role is very much concerned with pastoral care, and Susie connected with her class members on an emotional level. Right now, she was concerned about Jeannette, who had been made redundant and was having a crisis of confidence, and Marika, who had been suddenly widowed. The well-established classes were an enormous support, and that support was strong but unobtrusive. It is a curious factor of attending yoga classes that you can sit next to someone for years and never know their last name.

Susie was on her own spiritual path. She was fascinated by the healing aspect of yoga, and she had witnessed some amazing transformations during her career. One man called Bob came immediately to mind. Bob was a successful businessman, a high flyer. He was charming and charismatic, but the way he drove himself to succeed had taken its toll on his health. His blood pressure was sky high and he had severe lower back pain. His doctor recommended yoga classes and, although he was sceptical at first, he gave Susie a call. He was taken by her light and bright voice and her obvious enthusiasm for yoga. Susie offered him a free taster class and assured him that he could attend any of her ten classes in a given week. This meant that he could better fit it in with his work schedule. Fortunately, Bob chose a class where there were three other men, all of whom had been attending regularly for some time. He found his first class to be really interesting, and he booked immediately for the whole term. At first, he just enjoyed the peace and the fact that he could work with his body gently. It was the only place in his life where there was no competition, even with himself! This was a welcome novelty. Susie recommended alternate nostril breathing to lower the blood pressure, and working with the cat stretch and breath to ease the back pain. At first, Bob resisted taking yoga into his life, but when he began to notice the beneficial effects, he instigated a short daily practice. He noticed that when he stuck to his practice, his day simply went better. Other people began to notice, too, and that was a real joy for him. The tension between him and his wife eased, his children were more eager to spend time with him, and his work colleagues became more co-operative. He began to realise that there is more to this yoga malarkey than he had originally supposed. After his first year at class, Bob was feeling better than he had for years, and after five years, yoga had become his way of life. He was a great advocate of yoga practice, and he often invited Susie to give a seminar at his workplace – treating his employees to a day of stress-reducing techniques.

Susie's own path included making time for personal meditation. This was not always easy with a young family, but she was determined and would wake up at six, most mornings, to sit quietly before the day began. She had a special corner of her living room, where she could place her crystals or candles. It was her place of *Puja*, or ceremony. There she would hear the dawn chorus, the birds waking up and practising as a choir. Susie's meditation shawl came from India and was a treasured possession. She and Rob had visited India before they were married. They had done the Golden Triangle, and had also done some walking in Nepal. Later, Susie had made trips to an ashram. These times were very special to her; they were opportunities for her to accelerate her own spiritual growth. Rob was always enormously supportive, and they hoped one day to take the boys to India, too. The greatest joy of yoga is that it embraces all of you, and you learn to embrace all of you as well. So, some days you sit for meditation and watch your mind as it rushes round and round in circles. Other days, you have the most amazing experiences, realisations and guidance. Sometimes, you come out of your meditation with tears pouring down your face; and other times, you come out of your meditation with a silly grin, which stays painted on your face all day!

Several of Susie's students attended two classes per week. At first she had been concerned that they would not enjoy the same class, but this had proved not to be the case. Interestingly, she had her class plan beside her, as she had been trained, but it would alter a little in each of her ten groups. The energy of those present, and her own energy on that particular day, would have a bearing. One lovely young lady, who had a very serious illness, explained that her body knew what to expect on the second class, so she could progress much further. All yoga is based on awareness. Susie was emphatic that her students should work at their own pace and always be working with the body, never against it. If a student was tempted to push or force, then the body would clamp and defend. It was non-productive. Susie had realised, many years before this, that life is yoga and yoga is life. Pushing and forcing through life does not work either.

Susie was an only child. Her parents had followed a conventional pattern. They met at school, got along well together, and became a couple. The normal routine was to go out together for a few years, then to get engaged, and then to plan a wedding and a home together. This they did. Looking back, they would probably have both admitted that they drifted into marriage; it was not a grand passion, but rather an inevitable slide towards domesticity. Whilst there were no highs, there were also few lows, and their life together was comfortable enough. After two years of homemaking, Susie's mother, Marion, broached the idea of having a child. It seemed a simple enough progression, and Marion's pregnancy went well. Her husband, Jim, was ill-prepared, though, for the fierce rush of love he experienced when he first picked up his baby. It completely overwhelmed him. It felt somehow pagan – deeply resonant of ancestral love. He heard a celestial echo and he bonded with his child in a most moving, life-changing and profound way.

As Susie grew, this bond became ever deeper. Jim delighted in making her smile and chuckle. She took her first steps towards her daddy and clearly adored him. At first, Marion rejoiced in their close union but, as time went by, she began to feel excluded. Although she attended to the baby's every need, Susie's eyes were always on the lookout for Jim. She seemed to live for the moment when he came home from work. Marion mentioned having another child, when Susie was eighteen months old, but Jim would not consider it. His protective instinct towards his darling daughter, and his driving urge to provide her with everything that she could ever desire or need, was all-consuming. He would brook no argument on this point, and Marion was left feeling even more alone. She felt that perhaps another child would have brought balance to their family, but it was not to be.

Marion turned to her parents for support. She and her mother had a strong bond, a shared sense of humour, and enjoyed a good banter. Taking Baby Susie to spend time with her grandmother alleviated painful feelings for Marion, and she and her mother became even closer. All in all, she was resigned to the family dynamics, and if sometimes she experienced a quick flash of jealousy, she was ready to dismiss it or submerge it.

Susie was oblivious to the complications that surrounded her. She was loved. She knew, in the depths of her being that she was loved, treasured and protected. Her father was a cross between a god and a cuddly teddy bear; he had all the time in the world for her. Her mother, on the other hand, took care of everything for them. She cleaned and cooked and shopped and gardened. What else does a small child need?

Life went on. Jim started his own business restoring antique furniture. He was a superior carpenter and built Susie's doll's house for her. Later, he made a playhouse for the back garden, and he loved nothing better than to watch his little girl engrossed in make-believe domesticity. In some deep place in his heart, he would have liked to have frozen this time of his life, and his daughter's. He felt chills at the thought of her growing up, and even dreaded her first day of school. Their relationship was so perfect, how could he let her go? How could he allow even kindly, well-meaning teachers to plant new ideas in her beautiful little head? He never shared these thoughts with his wife. He feared that she would consider him to be obsessional, and that perhaps she would be correct.

Susie grew into a beautiful girl. She was sociable, outgoing and attracted friends easily. When her friends came to tea, her mother made them most welcome. If her father was a little quiet and withdrawn, she pretended not to notice.

Time passed; Susie moved from Junior School to Senior School. She spent more time with friends, became involved in after-school activities, decided to become a vegetarian. Jim watched with a protective eye, knowing that letting go was part of a parent's job. Seeing a child become independent was the parental aim, was it not? His head knew this, but his heart did not listen. He had a photograph of Susie at age four, playing with a doll's tea set, framed and placed on his desk. He would definitely have liked to have frozen her, and indeed himself, at that time. This, in his mind, was when his life was complete and meaningful. Meanwhile, Jim put little or no effort into his marriage. His wife had become accustomed to playing second fiddle to their daughter, and she now relied on her mother's love to nourish her.

Marion was capable; she was a good housewife and kept a good table. She was a reasonably attractive woman, not exactly a head turner, but, whilst the romantic side of her marriage had died at her daughter's birth, she was content with her lot. In moments of reflection, she realised that she wished for something more than this for her daughter. Perhaps the 'Happy Ever After' dream is pure fantasy? Perhaps everyone settles eventually for a fairly peaceful domesticity? And yet, surely intimacy on an emotional level is possible? Marion would like Susie to meet a good man. She would like her to meet a man who would care about her emotional needs; a man who would listen to her; a man who would be prepared to share his innermost dreams and fears.

Eventually, Susie brought boyfriends home. Jim had to admit to himself that his reaction was to be suspicious, possessive and surly. He became the disapproving father who refused to engage in conversation and who endeavoured to discourage prospective suitors. He did not like himself in this role, but he found it impossible to behave any other way. It was when Susie brought Rob home that he knew the game was up. Rob was a tall, slim and handsome guy, with a bohemian air about him. He approached Jim with his hand outstretched and with a big grin. Jim was compelled, momentarily, to take his hand and to meet his eyes. He saw only honesty and good humour in those grey eyes, and he knew the rival to his affections for his daughter had arrived in their lives.

Susie was in love. Her voice was brighter, her smile was wider; she glowed. It seemed to Jim that she even moved differently. She and Rob became inseparable, and it was apparent to her parents that this was the real deal. In some small, generous corner of his heart, Jim rejoiced for his entrancing daughter. How could he begrudge her happiness? The rest of his heart ached and, from his constant pain, an idea continually emerged: 'I could go.' It was as though his whole reason for being had collapsed. Every breath had been about protecting his little girl, providing for his little girl, making her laugh and hugging away her tears and disappointments. His future felt impossibly difficult. One morning, he simply got up and left.

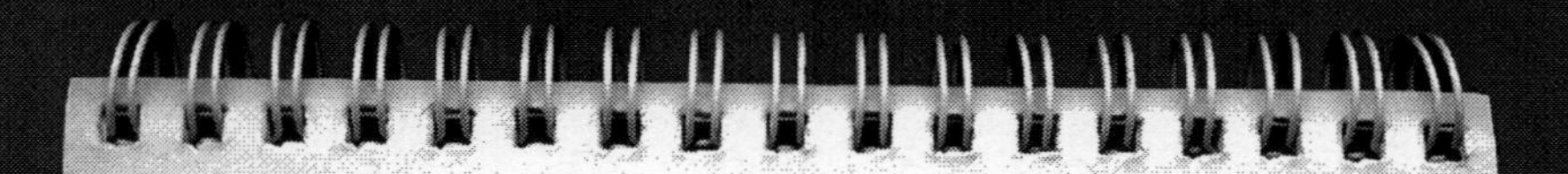

Suggestions from *Yoga Prescribed*

Alternate nostril breathing (or Nadi Shodhana) is helpful for lowering high blood pressure.

The cat stretch and breath exercise is useful for relieving a stiff and painful lower back. It is an important addition to any daily practice.

Visits to an ashram accelerate spiritual growth.

Meditation is the cornerstone to yoga practice and can be a most helpful daily routine.

Focussing on the sacral chakra will open you to creativity.

(All suggestions are based on anecdotal evidence and are in no way a substitute for medical advice.)

CHAPTER 4

ROB FINDS HIS PLACE

Marion did not realise that anything was amiss. Jim did not arrive home for his dinner, and she assumed that this was because he had become engrossed in the restoration of a particularly interesting piece of furniture. It was not until nine o'clock in the evening that she began to feel vaguely uneasy. By the time Susie and Rob bundled in, after being with friends at the local pub, she felt concerned enough to suggest that they phoned Jim's friend and employee, Martin. On hearing that he had not seen Jim all day and had assumed that he was out on a job, Susie broached the idea that they phone the local hospitals. At this point, they all still felt that Jim had merely forgotten to inform them of his movements. They had no reason to believe that anything awry had occurred. The hospitals reported no road accidents, and no patients with injuries that caused amnesia. They drew a blank and were compelled to wait until morning to phone the police.

Rob slept on the settee in the lounge that night. It seemed wrong to leave Susie and Marion, somehow. The house had a strange, expectant air and the ticking of the clock measured the hours for them all. At eight in the morning, Marion phoned the police and reported Jim missing. She had looked into his study and found that his favourite photograph of Susie, playing with her doll's tea set, at age four, was gone. His razor was also gone from the bathroom. She knew that, without understanding it for a single moment, Jim's exit from their lives was final.

The police could find no clue, and Susie went through agonies as hours turned into days and days turned into weeks. There was no word. She passed through the grieving process: anger, denial, acceptance and loss. How could the father who had always been her rock suddenly desert her? She missed him desperately and worried constantly, 'Where is he? How is he?' Throughout this time, Rob held her. He let her cry; he let her rage; he loved her. In quiet moments, when her love and gratitude for Rob overwhelmed her, Susie wondered if she had to pay for her happiness. Did she have to lose one man, whom she loved dearly, to be allowed to have another? In the depths of her heart, she knew that her father loved her. She knew that he meant her no harm; knew that somehow, in his mind, his disappearance was to protect her.

Marion did not miss Jim. He had become, at best, a mere shadow of a husband. Occasionally, though, she missed the father of her child. Jim had always been ready to fully engage with any discussion that had Susie's well-being at its core. Reality kicked in. Marion's little bookkeeping job was not enough to pay the mortgage, and she was going to have to make some serious decisions. Her father had been poorly for some time, and her mother needed help to nurse him. She decided to put their lovely house on the market and to move in with her parents. Their old rambling house could contain her and her daughter, and the old folk would be glad of the company.

The sale of her childhood home felt like an enormous step to Susie, although she knew that it made sense. On the day of the move, she said 'goodbye' to her playhouse at the bottom of the garden. She shed tears for her dad. How she missed him. A song from the show 'Aspects of Love' played through her mind and haunted her: 'I want to be the first man she remembers and the last man she forgets.' It was sung by a father about his daughter, and its words resonated deep in her soul. Fortunately, the new family moving in had three daughters who would love to take over the playhouse. It would be full of laughter once more.

Rob realised that his role in the family right now was to be the permanent man. He felt the call to represent the brotherhood. At only twenty-four he stepped up to the plate. On some level he recognised that he was in a unique position. Most people, on falling in love and joining a new family, wonder where they fit. Rob's place was clear to all. He bought the occasional gift for Marion: a small box of her favourite chocolates, a potted plant, a special soap. Marion found a new happiness in watching her daughter and her boyfriend, and she enjoyed their laughter and their love. She was discovering a deepening in her relationship with Susie, too. She had always been a daddy's girl, but now she turned to her mother for comfort and reassurance. Indeed, Susie discovered that there are three parties involved in parenting: there is the combination of father and mother; there is the father; and there is the mother. Marion was a different person, in Susie's eyes, once her father left home. She blossomed, laughed more, took more of an interest in her appearance. She even cooked more adventurous meals. She loved nothing more than trying out a new recipe on Susie, Rob and her parents.

A ginger kitten was abandoned in a garden near to where Rob's parents lived. Without giving his action too much thought, Rob scooped the little scrap up and took him to Marion. "I have a very special gift for you today, Marion," he announced as he entered the house. Susie's mother was filled with compassion, took the dear little life into her hands and dedicated her next few weeks to his nurturing. All the love that had been dammed in her marriage was lavished on the kitten, who they named Chico as he had a cheeky little grin. Chico soon had the household licked into shape, finding his favourite places and working out his timetable. He slept on Marion's bed at night, but during the morning would appear at her father's door to grace his bed and to keep him company. He ran to greet Susie and Rob, whenever they appeared, and had an individual call peculiarly his own.

Life went on, as life does. Susie learnt to live alongside the disappearance of her beloved father. She learnt to bury her grief deep in her heart. Years later, Alice was to suggest a flower remedy called Star of Bethlehem. This was enormously helpful, allowing Susie to release the grief. She never gave up on the idea that she would one day see her father again. Her biggest disappointment was that he would not be there to give her away at her wedding – and so she felt a bittersweet pang when Rob took her away for the weekend to Paris, booked an expensive restaurant and went down on one knee to propose. Rob was the love of her life. His sensitivity and devotion had been constant from the first time that she met him. He was clever, funny, outgoing and very good looking, in a long-limbed bohemian way. Susie loved his longish hair, his twinkling eyes and his sense of humour. There was never any doubt in her mind that he was the man for her, and that they would make a good life.

Marion was like a dog with two tails when she heard the news! She recognised that it was always going to happen, but the thrill of planning a wedding with her daughter filled her with joy. Her only concern was whether her father would live to see the happy day. He was failing fast. He was becoming forgetful, and losing all appetite. Her decision to move in with her parents had been the right one. She and her mother, Doris, shared the nursing and the work in the house. Marion's little job brought her in enough income so that she could contribute to the household expenses. The capital from the sale of her house, after the mortgage had been paid off, would both finance her daughter's wedding and be savings for her future. She would begrudge nothing for the big day. She wanted Rob and Susie to have all that they had ever dreamed about.

Rob looked at his mother-in-law to be with such affection in his eyes. He found her delightful. There is a saying that a young man should always look at his bride's mother to discover how his wife would turn out. He admired Marion and would never mind observing her traits in his wife. He recognised, perhaps more than Susie did, that Marion had been overlooked in her marriage. It had not been an easy road for her, and she had survived it, and being abandoned, with style. She had strength but also vulnerability. The way she was with Chico always filled Rob with affection. She had a lot of love to give.

This love wove its way through the wedding preparations. It was as though Marion's real career in life should have been a wedding planner! No detail was too small for her attention, and she kept a file meticulously to ensure that everything was documented. The highlight of the preparations was the day she and Susie went to London on the train to buy the dress. They walked till their feet burned, but eventually found just the right one. It had a Jane Austen feel to it. It was ivory in colour and covered in seed pearls. It showed off Susie's figure, and yet was ladylike and simple. It needed no alteration, as though it had actually been made with this pretty young lady in mind.

Susie bubbled over describing their day out in London to her grandparents, and quite suddenly her grandad's eyes filled with tears. "I will walk you down the aisle, sweetheart", he declared. Doris, Marion and Susie all immediately recognised the kindness of this offer but unanimously stated that it was impossible. They had not, however, taken into consideration the determination that Bill felt to do right by his granddaughter. He, William, would walk her down the aisle and he would stand beside her on her most important day. It was bad enough that her father would not be present; no way was her grandfather going to let her down, too. To everyone's utter amazement, he rallied from that moment, insisting that he would need a new suit and definitely new shoes. He was more than happy to leave talk of colour schemes, flowers and invitations to Marion and the young people, but he was adamant that he would be present at the church rehearsal.

So it was that Susie and Rob had the most beautiful wedding day. All eyes were wet as Grandad Bill took Susie's arm through his and walked, slowly but deliberately, up the aisle. There was never a prouder moment for him, or a more moving memory for the whole family. Susie looked utterly exquisite and Rob's heart burst with love for her. It was actually the happiest day of Marion's life, too – she who, as mother of the bride, had taken care of every detail of this event. The photographs were treasures, and the laughter and joy which infused the whole occasion lasted in the hearts of all those who were present. A long way away, Susie's father experienced a sudden lurch in his heart; a sudden very physical ache for his daughter. He knew not why.

Rob set about making his new wife happy, providing for her and supporting her. He fully recognised that for Susie to be content her mother had to be content, too. His role extended from young husband to loving son-in-law. The whole family saw his worth and welcomed him with open arms.

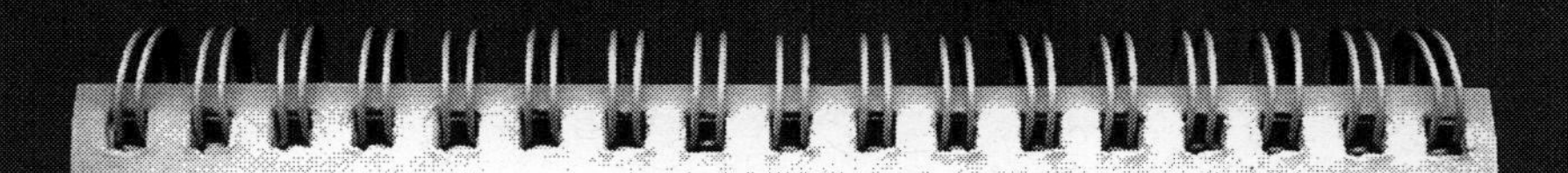

Suggestions from *Yoga Prescribed*

Flower remedies can be most helpful. Star of Bethlehem is good for grief.

(All suggestions are based on anecdotal evidence, and are in no way a substitute for medical advice.)

CHAPTER 5

WILLIAM, DORIS AND THE WONDERFUL SURPRISE

Years had passed since then, and Susie was now a busy mum and yoga teacher. She planned a class on the solar plexus chakra. This wheel of energy is concerned with willpower, and the first realisation that there is a mind as well as a body. Solar plexus means 'the place of the sun' and in modern times it is considered to be coloured a sunny yellow. Susie taught lots of spinal twists, to stimulate the chakra, and also the wonderfully invigorating Salutation to the Sun (known as *Surya Namaskar* in Sanskrit). She felt full of energy after these classes and brimming over with enthusiasm.

On the way home from her Wednesday morning class, Susie wondered just how much of her willpower came from her grandfather, William. He had been so determined to walk her down the aisle, and this he accomplished with style. He had enjoyed the whole day, bless him, and although Granny had kept a close eye on him, she need not have worried. Unfortunately, worry was suspended for a very short while. Three months after the wedding, William suffered a fatal heart attack. Doris, although she had expected this day for a long time, was numb with shock. You cannot live all your adult life with a man without being devastated at his demise. Indeed, Doris soon realised that you cannot experience emotions ahead of time. There is no preparation that can be made. All one can do is experience feelings fully in the moment. Susie recognised that her grandmother's connections to her long-time husband were through the chakras. They had a very strong connection through the heart chakra, but there were other connections, too, and some of them were very subtle. The occasional control issue and power struggle demonstrated the connection between their solar plexus chakras. Susie's granny was strong willed as well!

Granny Doris and Marion had continued to live happily together, both doting on their now fully-grown cat, Chico. Susie and her family were frequent visitors and, after Grandad's death, a new routine emerged. Marion became very interested in tracing the family tree. She spent many hours on the computer, researching William and Doris's parents and siblings. It turned out to be quite an emotional project, but she fondly persevered, imagining framing the finished tree for the twins, Toby and Max.

So at the exact moment that Susie was considering the chakra connections between her grandparents, her mother was researching the facts of their births. Families are always linked, and Susie had a strong belief in reincarnation. Yoga teaches that folk reincarnate in groups, so it is highly likely that everyone has interacted with their family members in a previous lifetime. Part of our life's mission is to heal our ancestors and to work out the karma left over from previous lives. Susie recognised the strong love and commitment that Doris and William had shared. She could readily see, now at her age, that her parents did not share a bond like that. Her thoughts strayed to her father again. Did he still feel the chakra connections with his daughter? When she thought of him, did he feel a pull? She knew little about *his* childhood, and *his* parents. Maybe he simply was not as grounded, as well planted, as she had been as a child. She had always known that she was loved and had felt as though the earth was firmly patted down around her. She had been sure to give her boys this same sense of security, and now delighted in telling them stories of when they were little. Her mother told the twins stories of their great-grandparents, and they always loved to hear how Grandad Bill had walked their mother down the aisle.

Doris and Bill had thoroughly enjoyed their Golden Wedding Anniversary. Now Susie was determined that Ted and Alice next door would do the same. They had managed to come up with a date that suited everyone – no mean feat! And they had invited Ted and Alice to lunch that day. The old couple did not suspect that trickery was afoot and that everyone was involved in a conspiracy to give them the best day of their lives. Rob had spoken to the bell-ringers and they had enthusiastically agreed to ring a peal on the special day. Susie had coaxed Alice into showing her their wedding album. She had asked to borrow it in order to show her mother, Marion. It was a ruse, of course, and the twins got busy copying photographs and getting them enlarged. They planned to have a display board at the village hall, and to decorate the room with the same flowers that Doris and her sister had lovingly arranged, fifty years before. Ted and Alice's daughter, Rosemary, wanted to order a huge cake and their son, James, was buying the champagne and wine. Susie, Marion and Doris would prepare a finger buffet, while Toby and Max would be checking that everyone had drinks. Toby and Max also planned some entertainment. They had their parents in fits of laughter at their skits and juggling antics. The boys tirelessly rehearsed, constantly building on their routine, and vying for which one of them would have the best jokes to tell.

The day arrived and their carefully laid plans were nearly blown when Ted looked in to offer them his home-grown asparagus for lunch. Although Susie was dressed prettily, there was no sign of preparations for a meal! Rob came to the rescue, ushering Ted out to the drive and talking about an oil smell in the car. Ted was soon distracted and, after a few minutes, he wandered home to change, still unsuspecting.

At the appointed time of midday, Alice and Ted arrived at the front door, and the twins begged them to come and see some badger tracks near the village hall. They readily agreed. They were somewhat surprised to see so many cars parked up near the hall, but in a flash they were bundled through the door and all inside yelled: 'HAPPY ANNIVERSARY'! Alice's stunned expression was caught on camera by her son, James, and she found herself engulfed in a huge hug from Rosemary. Ted managed to shake hands with Rosemary's husband, Jonathan, but would, as usual, avoid him for the rest of the proceedings. The old couple were treated royally by all present, and were so touched by their photographs on display and the carefully arranged flowers. Hilarity ensued when Max and Toby performed their well-rehearsed act. Then dancing began, with Rosemary's children leading Ted and Alice to the floor. It was such a special celebration; a day that fully recognised the time and energy that had gone in to their union; a day that fully recognised the special people that they were, together and apart. Their contribution to village life was hard to express, and the village turned out to appreciate them. The bell-ringers rang a peal of Grandsire Triples, and the church choir amazed everyone by singing a short medley of songs from the sixties, at the end of the event.

When Susie and Rob collapsed into their chairs later in the evening, they expressed their delight at how the day had unfolded. The twins had taken on the job of compiling an album of special photographs, and Rosemary and James had promised to email their candid shots. Ted and Alice had been celebrated in style. After the event, the old couple agreed to go to Watford. With their daughter, Rosemary, and her children, they would visit with their son, James. Rosemary's husband, Jonathan, tactfully spent time returning to his old haunts in London. Despite his efforts to be conciliatory, Ted was never going to make peace with his son-in-law!

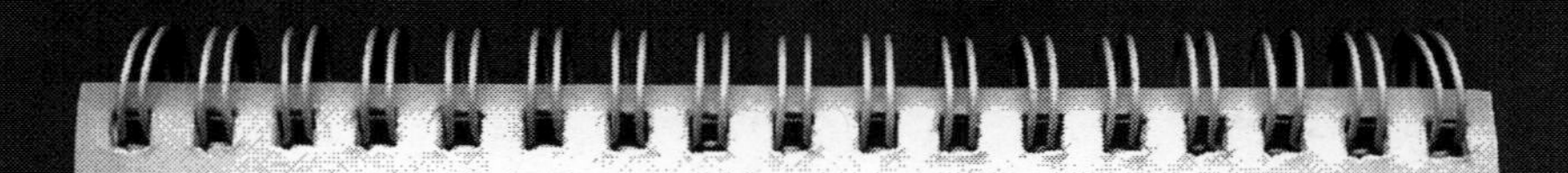

Suggestions from *Yoga Prescribed*

Salutation to the Sun is a classical yoga sequence that stimulates the solar plexus chakra. It balances the seven main wheels of energy, increases the suppleness of the spine, trims the body, strengthens the limbs and aids digestive problems.

(All suggestions are based on anecdotal evidence and yoga research.)

CHAPTER 6

SUSIE'S HEART AND A DIFFICULT WEEKEND

The yoga class that week was to be on the heart chakra. This is the wheel of energy in the centre. There are three chakras below the heart, known as the lower chakras, and three above, known as the higher chakras. This wheel of energy is said to be emerald green, according to New Age thinking, and it is all about unconditional love. Susie was naturally a very loving person and found it no effort to love her students unconditionally. This particular class, though, seemed to unlock some deep-seated emotions in her. The reading she had chosen for the beginning of the class brought tears to her eyes, and by the Thursday classes she was definitely experiencing a deep sense of loss. She wondered if this class, coming as it did straight after Ted and Alice's wonderful anniversary celebrations, was opening her heart in a new way. Normally, as Susie was a most professional yoga teacher, her focus was outwards. She saw her job as facilitating her students' spiritual progress. Clearly, though, this week's practice was touching a raw nerve. Susie took her sense of loss into her own early morning meditations and was surprised to find herself sobbing as she dissolved her practice. One morning, she awoke to find tears pouring down her face.

Rob was concerned to see his young wife looking low and decided that she was tired. She had worked tirelessly to make the

Golden Wedding party a success after all, and goodness knows two twelve-year-old boys can be exhausting. He suggested taking the twins away for the weekend to an activity centre, leaving Susie to catch up on her rest. She agreed to the plan, but regretted it almost as soon as they drove away. She felt unaccountably bereft. She sat in her chair and cried and cried. She felt as though her heart would break. Was this depression? She had never felt like this in her life before. Curiously, and completely out of character, she had no desire to see her mother or Alice next door. She simply wanted to curl up in to a ball and sob. This is how she spent the day and, although the cat did his best to engage her, she was oblivious to Pat's attentions. She dragged herself up to bed later and noticed she had a split which had opened up in her thumb. The split was really sore, more so than its size would indicate, and Susie noted that it was on her right hand. She well remembered her tutor telling her that the right side is the past and your father, whilst the left side is your future and your mother. She also recalled that the hand is about reaching out. Susie dropped into a restless and unsatisfying sleep. Her dreams were all about searching, searching. She woke up the next morning exhausted and drained.

Rob had asked everyone to leave Susie in peace for the weekend so that she could recharge. She felt that actually she was disintegrating, rather than moving up she was plummeting down in to a whirlpool of grief. She dragged herself from her bed, desperately wanting to bustle about, but finding that feeding Pat was all the effort she could raise. She slumped into her big chair, grabbed the box of tissues, and bawled. On another continent, her father lay desperately ill with dysentery. This she had no way of knowing. Well not on the conscious level, anyway.

Rob and the boys came home to find her still crying and bedraggled. He held her hand while she sobbed and struggled, incoherently, to explain how she felt. On some level he sensed that this was a deep wound and that it must be connected to Susie's dad. When the worst of this bout of crying was over, Rob left her and ushered the twins in to the kitchen to prepare a meal. The sound of their crashing and laughing lifted the energies in the house a little and Susie was able to sit at the table with them and to eat a small portion.

Susie got through that week with the help and support of her family and her yoga. One or two of her students noticed that she was subdued and lacking her usual joyful enthusiasm. She chose a meditation of silent repetition to honour that week's work on the throat chakra. The mantra 'OM MANI PADME HUM' had been a friend to her over the years. It was comforting to sit in silence with her students.

Rob watched over her, and he phoned her mum from work to chat about his concerns. He felt that the two women needed to explore the loss of Susie's dad together, so he suggested that they meet for lunch. Marion, understandably, was a little reluctant to open that particular can of worms, but if it would help Susie then of course she would talk.

They chose to meet on the Friday as there was only one class that day and Marion's mum, Doris, was going to a matinee with a friend. They would have the house to themselves. Marion prepared a simple but nourishing salad with raspberries and soya yogurt for dessert. They shared some elderflower cordial, moving in to the conservatory to sit comfortably. Susie explained her experience on the weekend, and acknowledged that it felt like deep-seated grief. She asked her mother if she ever missed her husband. Marion admitted that, no, she did not miss him on a personal level, but that she did miss sharing with him what was going on in Susie's life. She kindly stressed that Jim had always been a devoted father. Susie asked her mother if she still loved him. Marion had to confide that she remembered, with affection, the man she married, but that her love died of neglect long before he left her.

Marion said, "When Rob looks across the room at you his eyes are so full of love. Sometimes I feel that the love you two share is tangible. There is a channel between you and I feel that I don't want to walk across it, as I will disturb that wonderful current. And sometimes you look up at him with a teasing grin and a sense of absolute honesty. You know that he loves you, unconditionally, and that he always will. I never had that with your father. I knew that he loved *you* unconditionally, but I was not confident that he loved *me*. It was as though he could only find room in his heart for one person, and you, my darling, were that person. I did not begrudge you his love. If I am truly honest, I will admit that there were times in the early years when I felt the odd stab of jealousy. But it was more the fact of not being loved, and being confused by that, if you can understand?"

Susie nodded sympathetically. "Am I like him?" she asked.

Her mother paused, just briefly, and then replied, "Yes, occasionally, when you're explaining something to Max or Toby, I see a flash of Jim on your face. He had an enormous patience in his dealings with you, when you were little. Nothing was too much trouble. And sometimes when you laugh, I hear him. You and he used to laugh together all the time. In your character, I believe you take more after my side of the family. You are more well-rounded... He was a singular person, and I do believe now that he became obsessional about you. Don't get me wrong, his love was completely unconditional, he adored you, but his love was still somehow selfish. He seemed unable to share you. I really felt sorry for him, as you grew up. He seemed constantly confused by his own feelings."

Susie steered the conversation away to more normal topics. She was satisfied for now.

Later that day, the heaviness on her heart suddenly lifted. She still felt tired, and as though she had been ill and was still weak, but her good nature re-established itself. Rob was delighted to see her looking better and made sure he gave her some extra hugs that weekend.

Suggestions from *Yoga Prescribed*

Check where injuries or ailments are situated. It is said that the right side is your father and your past, while the left side is your mother and your future. This can help you to observe what is going on, holistically, in your life.

Repeating a mantra allows one to break through the everyday mind and to find the peace that lies beyond. OM MANI PADME (pronounced 'pay-may') HUM is a Tibetan mantra that has a profound effect.

Hugging is good medicine! It transfers energy and gives the person hugged an emotional lift. It is said that you need four hugs for survival, eight hugs for maintenance and twelve for growth. Scientists say that hugging is a form of communication because it can say things that you don't have the words for. And the nicest thing about a hug is that you cannot usually give one without getting one back!

(All suggestions are based on yoga experience and anecdotal evidence.)

CHAPTER 7

FAMILY AND THE PLUMP PIGEON

Ted had told the twins a story about pigeons. They had a particularly plump pigeon who regularly visited their garden. He feasted on the breadcrumbs and fat balls, and they used to joke that he took the whole garden as a runway to achieve flight. Ted told them that there was a very special pigeon called Ricardo Pompidou. His exploits were famous and tales of his adventures were passed down to each new pigeon generation. Ted charged the boys to listen carefully when the birds were cooing. He said that they would hear every pigeon's respectful recitation of their hero's name, "Ricardo Pompidou, Ricardo Pompidou, Ricardo Pompidou." Max and Toby were highly tickled by this story and by how many people they could hoodwink into believing it.

The twins had just celebrated their thirteenth birthday. They were now happily hurtling towards teenage challenges! Marion and Doris adored them but were finding it harder and harder to keep abreast of their lives and interests. Fortunately, Susie was well organised and got them where they should be, and Rob was always happy to transport them and their friends to football games and to encourage from the sidelines. The differences in their characters were becoming more pronounced. Susie found herself studying them carefully, one day, to see if she could see her father in either of them. Max was certainly talented with his hands, and he still loved working on a project with Rob. He may well have inherited his aptitude from his grandfather who was, after all, a Master Carpenter. Toby's creativity could be partly inherited from Grandad Jim, too. His flair for furniture restoration had been astonishing. Susie mused on family genes. She allowed herself a moment of indulgence, wondering how Jim would have interacted with his grandsons.

Meanwhile, Susie's episode had given her mother pause for thought. How responsible had she been for the failure of her marriage? After all, as the saying goes, it takes two to tango. Her biggest hurt was the fact that Jim left with no goodbye. That he had gone with no nod of recognition for the years that they had spent together and for the beautiful person that they had birthed. She was also astonished that it never crossed his mind to make sure they were taken care of financially. Granted he had never withdrawn any money from their joint account, but he tied up no loose ends and walked out on his business without a second glance. She allowed herself to wonder what his relationship would have been with the grandchildren, just as Susie had. If he had had the patience with the twins that he had always had with Susie, he could have shared his skills with them. "Ah well," thought Marion, "'what-if's' won't get the lunch cooked."

Marion was finding that more and more of her time was taken up with looking after her mother. She was running her around for appointments with doctors and specialists. Doris was looking more frail, and she took longer and longer to climb the stairs. Marion was not ready to part with her mother yet. They shared an unusually close bond. The work on the family tree had convinced her that her mother's stories of her childhood, and the extended family that she recalled, were crucial to her research. Marion decided to record her mother when she was in the mood to reminisce.

Meanwhile, for Toby and Max, there was a piece missing from the jigsaw of their family. They had never met their Grandad Jim. Their parents mentioned him, now and then, but he was just a shadowy figure in the background to them. They were fortunate to have excellent role models in Rob, Ted and Rob's father. Grandad Andrew was quietly supportive, and always ready to share a joke with the lads. Sometimes, though, they speculated about their lost relative. They created little stories about his exploits and where he was right now. They pondered as to whether he would suddenly turn up on their doorstep one day. And if he did, would they, on some level, recognise him? It was certainly abundantly clear, to anyone who knew Susie, Rob and the boys, that this errant grandfather was missing out.

The split in Susie's thumb had healed and then opened up again. Alice recommended calendula cream which definitely soothed, but did not heal the sore place. Then a split developed between two of her toes – on her right foot. This not only itched but burned, too, and Alice said to try tea tree oil. When her right hand then became covered in a rash, Susie realised that a deep-seated irritation was making its presence felt. She used Tiger Balm on the rash, which definitely alleviated the symptoms, but Susie knew that she had to spend some time in meditation delving to the root cause. Since all her problems were on her right side, she knew that it was to do with her father and her past.

Susie hoped that her current class on the third eye chakra, (*Ajna* in Sanskrit), would prove helpful. This one is all about intuition – teaching from within. Its colour is indigo, and Susie found herself instinctively wearing that colour. She encouraged her students to close their eyes and then to turn them up to look at the third eye, which is in between the eyebrows and in the centre of the forehead.

The theme of the yoga class the next week was the spiritual wheel of energy known as the crown chakra. Yogis say that this centre connects you to Spirit World and helps to open up an awareness of our assistants, whether they be guardian angels or spirit guides. The crown chakra is situated two inches above the top of the head and is considered to be lilac, although it is depicted as white in many teachings. The headstand stimulates this wheel, but yoga teachers always need to be careful about how they teach this posture. For some students, health conditions will prevent them from attempting it. A good yoga teacher knows his or her students really well, their health issues and general state of fitness. They have alternate postures up their sleeve for those who would be wise to avoid certain positions. Susie very much enjoyed the headstand herself, because she found that it was a powerful cleanser for her mind. She remembered her tutor saying that, "First thing in the morning, the thousand thoughts rush into the mind. Turn upside down and the thousand thoughts rush out again!" Chanting or repetition of a mantra is a powerful way of stimulating the crown chakra too and connecting with Spirit World. Susie had repeated the *Gayatri Mantra* so many times in her mind, that now when she woke up in the morning, it would already be playing. This is known as *Ajapa-Japa*. The Gayatri Mantra is one of the most famous ancient mantras in the world and is said or sung like this:

Om bhur bhuvah svah ha

Tatsavitur varenyam

Bhargo devasya dhimahi

Dhiyo yo nah pracodyat

The Sanskrit words can be translated like this:

> 'We meditate on the Supreme Sun whose light pervades this world (*bhur*), the heavens (*bhuvah*) and the next world (*svah*). May thy light guide our intellect in the right direction.'

It was on the Thursday early evening class that Susie particularly noticed Joanne. If a message came through, at the end of the long relaxation, to give 'so-and-so' a hug, Susie always obeyed. Inevitably, that person would be in need of special support. When she approached Joanne, she saw that her eyes were glistening with tears. She gently put her arms around her, and immediately Joanne's body was racked with silent sobs. Susie continued to hold her until the sobbing eased. Meanwhile the other students had quietly packed up their yoga equipment and had left the hall. Joanne had just a couple of minutes to collect herself before the second class of the evening arrived. Susie helped her roll up her mat and fold her meditation shawl. She made a mental note to phone Joanne a couple of days later.

It is not unusual to have a release after a yoga practice. It can be tears or laughter; it can be yawning or even itching. On some level, though, Susie knew that Joanne's release had opened a profoundly painful wound, and she felt that somehow it concerned her life as well as Joanne's. Just as her mantra continued to play at the back of her mind, so did this occurrence with Joanne.

Susie bumped into Alice the next morning. They shared a few pleasant words, just about the weather and the gardens, and then promised to meet up over the weekend. Alice invited them all in for afternoon tea on Sunday, if they were available. Susie loved the idea, and she promised to check it out with Rob and the boys.

After Susie's Friday morning class, she was free. She had some errands to do, but then stopped by to see her mother and her grandmother. Chico was the first to greet her, yowling as she opened the garden gate. Her mother was looking very well and was delighted to share the news that she had unearthed a long-lost cousin in the States. She was so enjoying her family tree journey. Doris, though, was not looking so well and Susie was reminded again that her grandmother was advancing in years. She made another mental note to spend more time with her. Susie's life, as a mother and full-time yoga teacher was a busy one. She loved everything that she did, but it was something of a juggling act to fit everything and everybody in. She was particularly committed, at this time, to her own *Sadhana* (her own spiritual practice). She badly needed time to explore her left side issues. Perhaps volunteering to drive her grandmother to some of her medical appointments could be an answer.

On leaving her mother and grandmother's house, Susie began to feel an urgent need to phone Joanne before the boys arrived home from school. Joanne answered the phone. She sounded subdued but very pleased to hear from her yoga teacher. She had been attending classes for a couple of years and particularly enjoyed the work with mindfulness and meditation. She loved the time when they sat quietly, as a group. That feeling of community had always been special for her. Now, quite quietly, she explained to Susie that this week's class had torn down a dam. Her emotions had swelled and released in a torrent. Susie remembered her tutor quoting the Chinese proverb, 'If your eyes don't cry, some other part of you will.' Joanne had been experiencing severe pain in her right shoulder. Her body was demonstrating to her that there was pain within that needed to be heard. Joanne continued to confide in Susie that her grief was about her son, Jack. He had always been the light of her life, and she was enormously proud when he went off to university to take a degree in History. He achieved a first, but his last year had proved stressful with a broken long-term relationship. He had returned home, with his possessions, but with no clear idea of his next step. Joanne and her husband endeavoured to explore options with him. They could feel that he was getting depressed and withdrawn. Then one day he just left. Susie was not prepared for the effect that this statement had upon her. Joanne's experience so clearly mirrored the exact same situation that she had experienced when her father left. Tears sprang to her eyes and her heart went out to Joanne. There was a moment of gentle silence, and then Susie suggested that they meet up for a cup of herbal tea and a good long chat. They had a soul connection, and although Joanne's grief was newer and more raw, they would be able to help each other. It would transpire that this help was to be of a more profound nature than either of them could have imagined.

Susie looked at her two boys with fresh eyes when they came home from school that afternoon. How precious they were to both parents and to the whole family. Dinner was lively and joyful, and the boys were full of their weekend plans, gladly making room on their calendars for tea with Ted and Alice.

Rob, Ted, Toby and Max began a competitive game of boules after this most delicious of afternoon teas. Susie shared her experience with Alice, mentioning no names, but explaining the similarities of the disappearances. Alice was a very wise lady. She loved people. She particularly loved Susie, and she was a superb listener. Alice could feel Susie's pain, still present after all these years. She heard an echo of guilt and knew that Susie still worried that she had to give up her father in order to have happiness with her husband. All relationships are so complex and if, like Susie, you believe in reincarnation, then you have an inkling that you might be working out past-life karma. This coincidence of circumstances had come into Susie's life right now, at this very moment, for a very important reason.

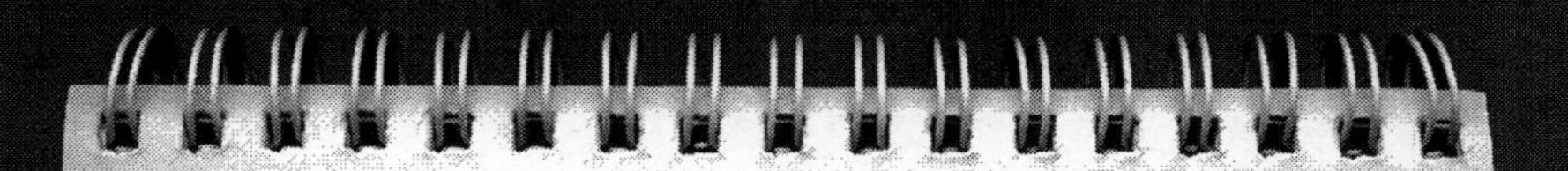

Suggestions from *Yoga Prescribed*

Calendula cream can be very soothing for the skin.

Tea tree oil is helpful for healing splits between the toes.

Tiger Balm can be used to ease stiff muscles, but it is also helpful for cracked lips and skin irritations.

The inverted yoga postures help to clear the mind.

Mindfulness and meditation are helpful for clearing the urgencies and clutter from the everyday mind. Meditating at the same time each day with a partner or in a group of three can have a powerful effect.

A Chinese proverb states that 'If the eyes don't cry, some other part of the body will.' Crying can be a powerful aid to healing.

(All suggestions are based on anecdotal evidence and are in no way a substitute for medical advice.)

CHAPTER 8

JOANNE AND THE JOINT VENTURE

This was the last week before half-term. There is a rhythm to the school year that Susie really enjoyed. At the end of six weeks of the twins in the routine of school and Susie in the routine of her yoga classes, they were all glad of a rest. Sometimes, Rob took the half-term off as well, and they enjoyed freedom and family togetherness.

During this yoga week, Susie was exploring Patanjali's Eight Limbs. Classical yoga practice is based on this wise teaching, a sort of system to follow and an aid to self-discovery. The first of the Eight Limbs is known as the *Yamas.* These abstinences give us a very real understanding of how to act ethically towards others, and the first of the Yamas is *Ahimsa,* non-violence or non-harm. Susie stressed that in yoga class we always work with our own awareness, never forcing or pushing, but working with the body and not against it. Therefore, we approach our postures with an attitude of non-harm towards ourselves. Traditionally, yogis are vegetarian. This reflects the same rule. You cannot eat a slice of cow without killing the cow first. This is violence. Many yogis become vegans, desiring only the well-being of all creatures, all beings. Vegans use nothing that has been taken from an animal. It fascinated Susie's students that the very first rule of yoga was an ethical one of such complexity. It may have been conjectured that the first rule would have been about the postures, or about the breath. In the East, of course, yogis grow up with the understanding that one's attitude to others is the first step to oneness. Yoga means union, and once we understand that if you harm another you are also harming yourself, we are on the road to enlightenment. Susie had chosen to work with sequences that flow with the breath. These sequences represent the way life flows, and the way that we can flow in our dealings with others. The feeling of goodwill in Susie's classes supported the feeling of co-operation and harmony that we seek in life. Susie lived her yoga. Her beliefs shone from her; her students saw that she glowed. Her yoga halls were filled with love and with peace.

Joanne felt this love and support on the Thursday evening class. She and Susie were to meet for a walk and a talk the next day. She was relieved to have talked to Susie about Jack's disappearance. She felt complete trust that she had confided in the right person.

It was a bright but cold day when they set out for their walk. Susie had often found that walking and talking was enormously beneficial. The fact that you are not face-to-face can be helpful, while being in the fresh air and nature has an opening effect. They had chosen to meet at a country park, where they were surrounded by beautiful trees. Apart from the occasional dog walker, they were undisturbed. Joanne talked more about her son. She spoke of how she desperately missed him. He had left her a very brief note, basically reassuring her that he would be safe and that she was not to worry. Susie blurted out that she and her mother had not had even that luxury when her father had disappeared. So, Joanne now began to realise their similar dilemmas. They talked openly, and lovingly, about their two lost family members. They met at soul level, and fully embraced one another's grief. Their mutual understanding was profound. They expressed compassion for each other, for themselves and for their errant relatives. It was almost incredible that these two special men had disappeared without trace, and apparently with no feelings of loss for the connection to their families. However, both women expressed a very real belief that they were all right. On some level, they were convinced that they would somehow have known if death or disaster had occurred.

As they continued to walk and talk, a small plan began to unfold. Might it be possible to contact their loved ones during meditation? Might it be possible to join forces? Is there a spiritual 'department' which aids seekers? This was ground-breaking work, but both women were keen to try. They had nothing to lose. They decided that their whole game plan was not to put pressure, spiritually or otherwise, on their loved ones. They simply wanted to discover that they were safe. And so they parted that day with a big hug and a promise to keep in close touch.

Joanne felt good as she drove home. She was no longer alone and, whatever happened in the future, Susie's warm-hearted friendship would be an enormous comfort. Joanne's husband was late coming home that night. Mark was a go-getter and led a stressful business life. He was in no mood to discuss the 'flaky' idea of contacting his son during meditation. He would actually have preferred to employ a private detective. Joanne let the subject drop, nursing her own beliefs tightly in her heart.

Joanne and Mark owned a dog called Jim. He was a lovely cream-coloured Standard Poodle. Poodles are remarkably intelligent and sensitive, and Jim seemed to be able to gauge when Joanne was most missing Jack. He would place his chin on her knee and gaze lovingly into her eyes. His favourite place to sleep was still on Jack's bed, which Joanne did not discourage. She felt that, somehow, he was keeping a welcome ready for Jack's return. It had struck both the ladies that it was extraordinary that Joanne's beloved dog should have been given the name of Jim, five years earlier, as it was the same name as Susie's father. Now, when Joanne called Jim, while out on a walk, she always thought of

Susie and her dad. Next time she met Susie for a walk, Joanne determined to take Jim, too.

Finding time for the agreed meditation was not a problem for either of the ladies. They both felt that it was important to schedule it at the precise same time. This was a priority, and they adhered stringently to their programme. Occasionally, they would 'catch eyes' across the yoga hall, and share a secret smile.

At first, Joanne began her meditation time by watching her breath, but after a few days she chose to sit in her heart instead, and to listen to what her heart whispered to her. There was a special place in her heart that belonged solely to her son. *Hasta Mudras*, or hand positions, are seals or gestures which alter the consciousness and create a psychophysical change. She used the heart mudra – a hand position known as *Hrdaya Mudra*. This was said to relieve an over-burdened heart, on the physical level as well as on the emotional level. If she could contact Jack at all, it would be through their hearts. They had always been close and Joanne was a loving mother. As she moved deeper into her meditation, she sometimes had flashes of colour or brief images visiting her inner eye.

Susie had explained that she was beginning her meditations with a mantra. She was using 'OM NAMO BHAGAVATE VASUDEVAYA' which was said to bring success to all ventures. She had confided that nothing extraordinary had yet occurred but she was convinced that time and patience would pay off.

Joanne began to feel great concern for the journey that Susie had been travelling. The depression that she had experienced when Jack disappeared began to ease as compassion for another replaced it. How difficult must it have been for Susie? To lose her beloved father and not to have any idea where he was, or even if he was okay, must have been a severe trial. The fact that Susie had gone on with her life and become the beautiful soul that she indeed is, filled Joanne with admiration. She understood how important yoga had been in supporting Susie, and how, through her yoga, she had helped so many other people. Susie lived her yoga, adhering to the ethics and philosophy. Belief so strong is a structure that supports. Within the discipline of yoga there is enormous liberation. Joanne fully appreciated how fortunate she was to have found a teacher who fully embraced the yoga way of life, and who so generously shared her convictions and love with others. The fact that they shared a common grief also fascinated Joanne. They were meant to meet in this lifetime; they were meant to work out their life questions together. Joanne felt that it was karma.

Susie broached the subject of inviting Joanne and her husband round for dinner. Rob agreed readily as he had heard so much about Joanne and her son, Jack. They chose an evening when the twins had been invited for a sleepover. It was a fourteenth birthday bash, and the boys hoped to camp in their friend's garden. If the weather was fine enough for that, it would also be clement for sitting in the garden for at least a cocktail before their supper. Joanne was delighted with the invitation. She was curious about the two husbands meeting and wondered if they would click, as she and Susie had.

Sure enough, the evening of their dinner arrangement was fine and mild. Susie and Rob prepared the sun deck for their first drink. They chose the evening's menu carefully. Being vegetarians themselves, the food they offered to guests was vegetarian and nutritious. Susie paid full attention to colour, bringing in the idea of rainbow colours. She had long been aware that she was attracted to orange foods, such as carrots and satsuma oranges, if her sacral chakra was out of balance. She knew that the evening would be a new experience for Mark, and she kept her fingers crossed that he was open-minded! This proved to be the case. From the first handshake Susie could tell that Mark was eager to connect with these new people in Joanne's life. He spoke quickly, had a great sense of humour and a mischievous twinkle in his eye. He talked to Rob about the boys and their love of football. He mentioned that his son, Jack, had been a keen cricketer at fourteen, and it was then that his face clouded over. He looked weary, just for a moment, and older than his age. Rob was a genial host, friendly, gracious and sensitive. He steered Mark past the difficult moment and topped up his glass of wine. They began to discuss the garden. They admired Ted's vegetable patch, over the fence. Joanne kept a close eye on the two men, until she had sized up Rob. Her first impression of him was much as she had expected. He was long-limbed, bearded and bohemian in appearance. He had a ready smile and moved quietly. His voice fascinated her. There was a depth to his tone and a kindness to the words he chose. Occasionally, when he caught Susie's eye, Joanne could feel the love between them. She knew that it was the right decision to introduce Mark to her new friend and to spend time with these special folk.

After a delicious supper of sweetcorn chowder, avocado and cashew nut salad, and apple and date crumble with natural soya yogurt, they sat comfortably and the subject of mindfulness cropped up. This was often mentioned in the yoga classes but Mark was new to the idea. Susie explained that being mindful was being aware of every moment; of being truly present in every moment. So, if you are doing the washing-up, then that is all that you are doing. You are not doing the washing-up to clean the kitchen, you are not doing the washing-up so that you can go out afterwards, you are simply doing the washing-up. There are two aspects to this mindfulness practice that Mark immediately grasped. The first is that that, instead of racing through your life at break-neck speed with your mind hurtling from one subject to another, you completely engage with each activity. This gives you a sense of space and each task is done completely and efficiently. The second aspect is that everyone can cope with just this moment. It is when we are regretful or pained by our past, or anxious and fearful for our future, that we resist being in the present at all. Mark's busy business life would benefit from this new approach, and Joanne had an inkling that their relationship could receive a well-needed boost as well. They had dealt with the disappearance of their son in very different ways. Joanne had become withdrawn, depressed and had grieved. Mark had buried himself in his work, becoming irritable and short-tempered. The couple had a sense that being around Susie and Rob could bring a new balance into their lives. Mark very much enjoyed the way Rob gave his wife space and respect. He was quite ready to question her about her beliefs, but it was done very lovingly. There was the sense that this couple never stepped outside of the 'loving circle'. There was the sense that they put love first; indeed that the fuel used to run the family and their household was love itself.

Joanne and Mark left Susie's lovely country home feeling refreshed. They had not raised the subject of Jack or Jim as that was for the future. Both couples felt more than content that they had embarked on a new friendship and that the evening had gone really well.

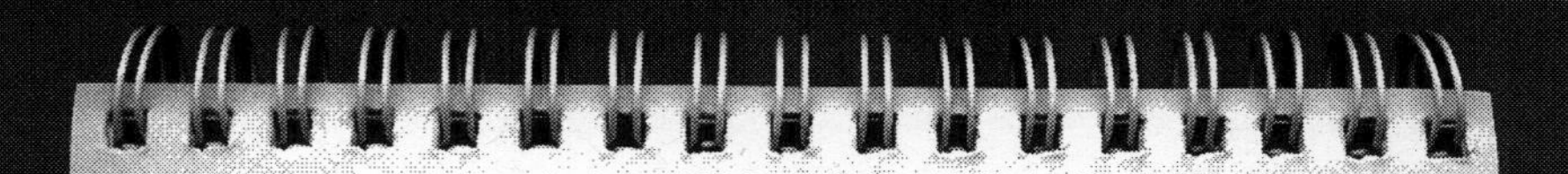

Suggestions from *Yoga Prescribed*

Learning about the yoga philosophies, such as the Eight Limbs of Yoga set down by Patanjali, can be very helpful for giving one's life meaning.

Walking and talking can solve many problems.

Hasta mudras are hand positions that work on the meridians of the body. Choose one and work with it daily. The effects can be amazing. Dhyana Mudra empties the mind. It looks like an empty bowl with the hands cupped, left hand on top of right, and the thumbs touching. The hands rest comfortably in the lap. (It is said that women should have the left hand on top and men should have the right hand on top. I have found, however, that both sexes benefit by having the left hand on top during meditation and quiet times. This way stimulates the feminine side, which is calming and mystical.)

Creating and maintaining a 'loving circle' in the family is an exercise worth cultivating.

(All suggestions are based on anecdotal evidence and yoga research.)

CHAPTER 9

DORIS AND THE DISCLOSURE

Marion woke up with a horrible cold and decided to take Susie up on her kind offer to drive her grandmother to her hospital appointment. Fortunately, the timing worked with Susie's yoga classes, and she was glad to spend some one-on-one time with Doris. Susie reminded her mother about tongue scraping and the practice of *neti* (nasal washing). Both can help to keep colds at bay, and were part of Susie's own early morning routine. She gently settled Doris into the car and drove smoothly so as not to jar her back. Although her sense of humour was still intact, Doris was finding her days a little more challenging. She was delighted to live with her daughter, and counted her blessings regularly. How would she manage without Marion? Of course, they had their moments! Doris had set ideas about how the kitchen should be run, and these did not always coincide with Marion's views. And there were times when Marion had just taken the weight off her feet, and had sat down comfortably, when Doris would desperately need a cup of tea or would announce that she had lost her glasses. Marion found this perverse and definitely irritating, but nevertheless, for the most part, they rubbed along together very happily.

Susie ruminated on the idea of growing older. If there had been a 'human model', engineered and fit for purpose, then all parts would have worn out similarly. This was not the case. Some older folk experienced hearing loss. Some folk developed arthritic joints. Some had heart problems. There had to be more to this aging process than at first met the eye. Yoga had a lot of the answers, and Susie wondered if she could, at some point, set up a class specifically for older people. It fascinated Susie to contemplate that past lives and the way we hold on to our issues in this lifetime both influence the way the body ages. But perhaps the most influential aspect to aging is attitude and spirit. Those with a positive, upbeat attitude approach aging differently and it is certain that the body manifests what is going on in the mind. She thought to herself how remarkable it would be to set up an old yogis' home, and to chart a spiritual approach to aging and to dying. Susie planted this seed of an idea at the back of her mind until she had time to explore it in greater depth.

Doris was in the mood to chat. She did not often have Susie to herself, and she asked Susie if she had ever known that her mother had a brother? Susie replied in the negative, with a very surprised arch of her eyebrows. Doris misted over a little when she mentioned her son's name, Barry. He was younger than Marion by two years and had died in an accident. The local children had been playing on the village green, as they did most days. Barry was just five, but Marion kept a good eye on him, while Doris could see them from the front-room window. There was a big old sprawling tree there, and some of the bigger boys would climb it easily, to gain a great vantage point. One day, while Marion was busy skipping and chanting the songs the girls all knew, Barry begged the big lads to help him climb the tree. They did and he was thrilled, but one wrong step and that was it. The boy holding his hand, Richard, did his very best to save him. But it was no good. He fell and he landed with a sickening thud on the ground. Marion ran to him, Richard ran for Doris, and Doris screamed for Bill. Barry had landed on his head and was dead when the ambulance arrived. Their whole community went into mourning. Barry was a dear little chap. He'd been full of mischief and he had always had a twinkle in his eye. He had been so friendly and affectionate that everyone missed him. As Doris raised her handkerchief to her eye, lost for a moment in vivid memories, she was called in to see the doctor.

Susie was momentarily stunned. How incredible that she had never known that she had had an uncle. Of course, he would feature on the family tree. She had only paid scant attention when her mother had talked to her about plotting it, but her curiosity was certainly aroused now!

Doris returned from her appointment, sharing a chuckle with the nurse, and Susie took her back out to the car. On the way home, she parked at a local viewpoint, and they gazed out over the countryside below. "Tell me more about Barry and how you all coped after his death, Grandma," Susie requested.

Doris was only too willing to disclose how agonised she was, and how overwhelmed by grief and guilt. She described how the questions constantly played in her mind: "Why was I not out there to say, 'No, don't climb the tree'? Why was I not looking through the window in time to run out and catch my little boy? Why, oh why, did I allow the children to play out, unsupervised?" Doris had slid into a deep depression. The funeral became a blur in her mind and she was unable to function properly.

Her husband, Bill, was slightly more resilient. He had to keep working, and it fell to him to keep the family together. He had to put his grief to one side and to live alongside it. After a while, he had sat Doris down and said, "You have a beautiful little girl who desperately needs you, sweetheart. You must rally. How do you think Marion is feeling? She is not too young to feel guilt. She has lost her beloved little brother and now it must feel that she has lost her mother, too."

Doris knew in her heart of hearts that he was right. She did rally, and she took up her role as Marion's carer and protector once more. They cried together, and they tended Barry's grave together. If Doris held Marion just a little bit tighter, and if she was a little more reluctant to part with her at the school gate, that seemed only natural. As for Marion she kept her own counsel, but she had begged for one of Barry's sweaters and dressed her teddy bear as Barry. Looking back now, with the wisdom of hindsight, Doris's heart broke open to think of both her children at that time. She said that when Jim had left Marion, so suddenly, she did consider that this loss must have resonated with her previous loss. She also wondered if Marion had suffered with a sort of surviving sibling syndrome. Did she feel guilty that she had survived while Barry had died? Did she ever worry that her parents might have preferred it if it had been the other way round? She had always been such a good little girl, she never rebelled, and she was quiet and subdued, never putting herself forward. Doris queried whether she had been like this in her marriage. When Jim became obsessed and all-loving towards Susie, his little daughter, had Marion given up too readily? Had she accepted the role of second best, because this was a role with which she felt familiar?

These thoughts played on Susie's mind as she drove her grandmother home. She gave her a special hug when they parted, and thanked her very much for this confidence. Susie wanted to do some thinking before she talked to her mother about all this. She wanted to run it past Rob, too. Her life was a busy one. She had all her yoga classes, her teenage twins, a home to run and yet it had come into her consciousness again this morning that Grandma was getting older and would not be around forever. Somehow, she must spend that quality time with her. She must listen to her stories. Susie was seeing her mother's life in a different context after Doris's disclosure. She wondered if her mother had ever told Jim about her little brother. Did they ever share like she and Rob did?

Susie was still working on the first of the Eight Limbs in her yoga classes that week. These are the Yamas, and they talk about how we should behave towards others. Her students had embraced *Ahimsa*, non-violence, and were now exploring *Satya*, truthfulness. Susie was aware of learning new truths about her family and the dynamics between her parents. One truth that Susie embraced fully was that she loved her family dearly: Rob, the twins, her mother and her grandmother. She pledged to tell them this more often.

Susie also loved her friends and her students, and was amazed and delighted to return home to an answerphone message from Joanne. Her son, Jack, had come home!

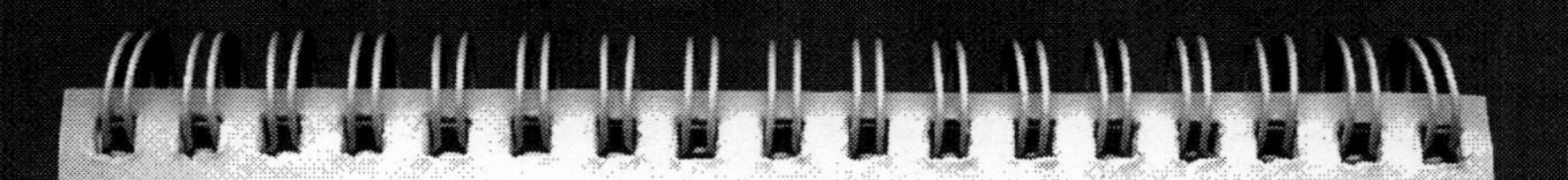

Suggestions from *Yoga Prescribed*

Cleansing the tongue with a special scraper is an interesting process and should be done first thing in the morning. Gently stroke the implement from the back of the tongue to the front. In addition to cleaning away germs, it is said that the 'gag' reflex, which sometimes occurs, cures depression.

Neti is a practice that involves washing the nasal passages with saline. A neti pot is like a small teapot and is filled with warm water and a little salt. (Bicarbonate of soda can be used instead of salt, if the nasal passages are tender.) Leaning over the bath and turning the head to one side allows one to insert the spout of the neti pot into one nostril and to pour the liquid through. It will come out of the other nostril. Then repeat the process inserting the spout into the second nostril. When finished, close one nostril and breathe in and out rapidly through the other one to dry it. Then repeat with the second nostril. Neti is very helpful for people who work closely with children and the general public, for instance, and who are constantly bombarded with cold germs. It is also most helpful for those who suffer with allergies. (Neti should never be performed if a sinus infection is present.)

(All suggestions are based on anecdotal evidence and should not replace medical advice but rather support it.)

CHAPTER 10

YOGA AND HOW YOGA TEACHERS ARE USED

Jack had arrived home the previous evening. He had breezed in, just as he used to as a teenager, shouting, "Hi, Mum!" Joanne was overwhelmed with relief and with love. She could hardly believe her eyes and her ears. 'Jack's home', 'Jack's safe' – these words kept playing in her mind. She was almost afraid to ask any questions, as though somehow he could disappear again if she pressed him in any way. But Jack was pleased to talk and to explain, and they sat a long time over a cup of tea and talked frankly.

Jack felt that he could not breathe at the end of his degree course and after the break-up of his relationship. He could feel himself getting lower and lower and somehow the effort of even talking about it was just too much. He had felt that he would drown if he did not leave. He caught his mother's eye and apologised for the worry that he had caused her, but he stood by the fact that he had had to leave or go under. He had done some fruit picking and then worked as a farm labourer. His instinct was to work manually, to be close to the earth. He'd talked little and just concentrated on putting one foot in front of the other. He'd simply got up each morning, used his physical strength all day, and then fallen exhausted into bed at night. Jack said that he'd let his mind freewheel. He'd found that performing repetitive, mechanical tasks was just what he needed. Joanne could feel the truth in what her son was telling her and she admired his intuitive understanding of his psychological state. She consciously stayed in the moment with him. She was determined not to talk about the future or what he felt he would do next. Here they were, sitting and talking. It was enough. Actually, it was more than enough; it was everything.

Joanne's husband, Mark, came home and could barely believe his eyes. He checked a rush of irritation and indignation at Jack's lack of consideration, and he settled for a big bear-hug of welcome instead. The three of them shared a bottle of wine. They talked long in to the evening. Eventually, Mark and Jack made their way to bed and to sleep, but Joanne's mind was far too alive to allow her to lie still. She wandered around the house, standing for a while outside Jack's bedroom, listening to his deep breathing. She sat in the lounge with Jim, their poodle, until he eventually made it clear that he wished to sleep and would she please go away now! Eventually, she climbed into bed and repeated her mantras before falling asleep with a grin on her face.

The next morning, Joanne left an answerphone message for Susie. She so wanted to share her good news with her. Susie had been her soul mate through this difficult six months, and Joanne was convinced that their joint meditations had had an effect.

When Jack had slept out his sleep and then had a shower and dressed, they settled down to talk some more. He was tentative at first about sharing a particular experience that he had had. Three weeks earlier he'd woken in the middle of the night, his eyes bleary and sleepy, and he had made out a figure sitting on the bottom of the bed. (He was staying as a lodger in one of the farm cottages at the time.) The figure was his mother, it was Joanne, and she was smiling gently at him. Jack explained that it reminded him of when he was five years old and he'd had measles. He had woken then, from a feverish and fitful sleep, to see his mother quietly sitting on the bottom of his bed, watching over him. In his vision, three weeks ago, she was silently mouthing words. Her eyes were almost closed and she had a serene expression on her lovely and familiar face. Jack said, "It was truly remarkable, Mum. You were there. Your presence, your energy, your spirit were all present."

Joanne told Jack then about the meditations that she and Susie had been doing, and about how comforting for her it had been to have a companion through this time. Jack grinned. He had always teased her about her yoga classes but he was getting an inkling now of how powerful belief and practice can be. It was the day after the 'visit' from his mother when Jack decided he was ready to go home. He was on track and able to face getting back into his life. Joanne would have plenty to tell her yoga teacher when they met for a walk and a talk!

Susie was thrilled with Joanne's news and they shared a long and meaningful hug. Joanne looked ten years younger as the worry dropped from her shoulders. It was just such a huge relief to know that Jack was safe. She gave full credit to yoga, and to their partnership meditations. She sincerely felt that she had been helped to find a way of connecting her energy to Jack's and, by doing so, had been able to remind him of how much he was loved. Susie remarked once again that there is more to this yoga practice than meets the eye. She remembered the theme of her classes that week – *Asteya*, non-stealing. (This is the third of the *Yamas* or abstinences. The Yamas form the first category in the Eight Limbs of Yoga.) She would not steal the tiniest drop of Joanne's delight by thinking about her father and of how much she would love it if he suddenly appeared home.

This episode was one of so many that Susie experienced in her life as a yoga teacher. A chance comment from a student could result in a realisation in a meditation, or a change of direction in class. Susie had learned to trust her inner guidance, and she sometimes found herself saying things that completely amazed even her! She learned to pass on visions and messages, regardless of how bizarre they appeared, and she discovered just how open and receptive her students could be. There is a great deal of pastoral care associated with being a yoga teacher, but it never feels onerous. It is as though Spirit World uses these teachers as a vehicle, a way in. The fact of the matter is that the yoga teacher, too, is learning and growing. Their lessons come with the energy shifts that occur amongst the students. They are all evolving together, as their energies become finer and finer. Susie was to see how her experience with Joanne would have repercussions in her own life.

Life continued on, full and busy. The twins were growing up. Sometimes, around the dining-room table, the family had lively discussions on subjects such as reincarnation. Toby was a believer, like his mother, but Max was not. One aspect of yoga practice that both boys embraced was the breathing exercises. *Pranayama* is an important aspect of yoga, and the Pranayama exercises, such as *Bhramari* the bee-breath, really helped the twins with their sports. They had a good understanding of their bodies and an instinct to embrace complementary medicine approaches to any health issues. Toby was particularly interested in the concept of *prana*, which the yogis describe as life force, or life-giving energy. He remembered, from his mother's children's yoga classes, that prana is gathered by the air that you breathe, by the food that you eat, from the sun and the earth. He certainly had discovered that some of the breathing exercises (especially if used first thing in the morning), gave him more stamina. It had taken him a few attempts but he had mastered *Kapalabhati*, which involves pulling the abdomen in sharply to briskly release the out-breath through the nostrils. Then he allowed the abdomen to relax and the in-breath would take place. The exhalation was active and the inhalation was passive. Toby did three rounds of this in the morning, with twenty pulls of the abdomen each time. It cleared his head for study, and it seemed to improve his stamina on the football pitch.

Susie maintained that the two conditions that improved almost immediately with yoga were back problems and breathing problems. She, like her tutor before her, was convinced that all health problems were based on stress. Even the first few yoga classes teach a student awareness of the body, giving them an insight into what real relaxation feels like. Susie well remembered one student who came out of her first ever yoga relaxation with a huge grin on her face. "I have never relaxed before, in my whole life!" the student had exclaimed. "And I had no idea how rigid I was, until I let go, followed your words and actually relaxed."

The breath is the key to relaxation, to meditation and to moving from the physical to the spiritual. Whatever the reason a student has for joining a yoga class in the first place, invariably they remain in the class for an entirely different reason. Yoga opens for them new layers of understanding. Some of Susie's students had been with her for more than fifteen years now. They knew that if they attended a yoga class once a week, their week simply went better. Whether they began because of persistent back pain, or because of breathing problems, they stayed because the holistic approach of the yoga practice improved their feelings of well-being on all levels.

Susie was thrilled to see one of her sons embracing the Pranayama practices. Her boys had grown up in a yoga household, where the basic beliefs and philosophies were on offer. They recognised that their family home felt a little different to that of their friends. They laughed together, played together, and there was a great deal of positive affection on display. In other homes, they were aware of stress and short tempers. That is not to say that Susie and Rob never became tetchy. They were human, after all! But this was unusual, rather than being the norm.

Toby had made a friend of one of the children in Susie's junior yoga class. This boy, Matthew, suffered from really bad asthma. It prevented him from playing football and running with the other lads. He was slim and pale, and was becoming quite introverted, when a friend of his mother's suggested that he joined a yoga class. He took to it immediately, recognising that there was no competition in yoga and therefore he could be a participant. Susie taught Matthew to pant like a puppy-dog. This helped him to focus on breathing out. Asthma has the effect, for the sufferer, of feeling that they cannot breathe in, so there is a feeling of panic: 'I can't breathe, I am going to die'. Actually, the in-breath cannot take place because the asthmatic has not exhaled completely and, therefore, there is no room in the lungs for more air. Mastering the puppy-dog panting breath gave Matthew two new tools: firstly he eased the breathing difficulty physically, while secondly it gave him a feeling of being more in control. The asthma was no longer happening to him, he was owning the asthma and recognising that he could be responsible for alleviating it. Just having something to do is a distraction for the mind and for the emotions.

Susie also introduced Matthew to mandalas, which are beautiful geometric drawings designed to aid mental concentration and lead you to meditation. He became so fascinated by them that he began to create them at home. His mother noticed that he would often draw a picture after a particularly bad asthma attack. She began to keep his mandalas in a folder, dating them and giving a brief comment on Matthew's health at the time. When Toby called round to play with Matthew, they would spend time out in the garden practising the yoga postures that they had learnt at their last class. Toby was always amazed at the way Matthew could balance. It seemed that asthma had taught him patience, and it was incredible how long this youngster could hold the tree pose, standing effortlessly on one leg. Toby's attempt to emulate the achievement usually ended with them rolling round the grass in fits of laughter! It was perhaps his friendship with Matthew that had provoked Toby's own fascination with the yoga breathing exercises.

Susie's whole way of life was yoga. It was as though she wore glasses with, instead of rose-coloured lenses, yoga-coloured lenses. She had an inbuilt desire to help others, and her way of doing this was through her yoga teaching. It did not finish at the door of the yoga hall, though. Susie took all her knowledge forward and shared it with everyone with whom she came into contact. She saw opportunities to promote yoga's beliefs constantly, in her family, with her friends and with her neighbours. Yes, she shared ideas and observations with her teenage sons, but also with her aged grandmother, Doris. She and Alice, next door, could talk for hours about folklore, herbs, and anecdotal evidence of cures for all sorts of illnesses. Susie loved to discuss the tools that yoga 'prescribed', or offered, to alleviate many different conditions.

She was sitting in the garden one day with Alice talking about the fact that back pain sufferers and asthma sufferers generally benefited very quickly from yoga practice, when Alice introduced the subject of cancer. One of her close friends had just died from lung cancer and Alice had been deeply sad to see her in pain and in distress. "What is your take on cancer, as a yoga teacher?" Alice enquired.

Susie thought for a moment before replying, "Well, I hear that one person in three will be diagnosed with cancer in their lifetime. It is the disease of our time, and some of my students have journeyed through the illness and the treatments. It seems to be that the whole of yoga is based on the premise that we listen to our bodies, never forcing or pushing, but always working with the body. When you read that someone is 'battling against cancer', it makes me very uneasy. I sincerely believe that every cell in our bodies wants the host to continue. Otherwise, they are signing their own death warrant. I read once that this is why the body endeavours to contain the cancer in one area. That might be the breast or the testicle. The whole body realises that it has a problem, so it makes a plan to isolate that problem for the good of the whole. Cancer cells have transmuted from their normal form because they are not receiving oxygen or, as we would say in yoga, 'prana'. They have to adapt or die. Apparently, cancerous cells can be identified in the body of a pregnant woman. They are there to break down the wall of the uterus so that the umbilical cord can firmly attach. In this case, these cells are pro-life. What always amazes me is that folk I know well, those who have been open to complementary therapies and who are really spiritual, receive that diagnosis of cancer and immediately are seduced to follow the medical route."

Alice nodded. She felt, like Susie, that the body had its own healing plan, in all circumstances. "Is there anything you do to positively support your own body, with reference to cancer?" she asked.

"I take three apricot kernels every day on my cereal," Susie replied. "I attended a talk, given by a medical journalist, which made a striking impression on me. He maintained that the B17 vitamin contained in apricot kernels terminated the perfectly normal activity of cancer cells. I believe in it, so I do it. I have to be cautious about telling others about this. After all, we are all on a journey of self-discovery, and it is essential that we all listen to our own inner teacher, our inner guidance. When you think about the word 'intuition' and break it down, it is teaching or 'tuition' from within. But I am convinced that fifty years from now, medics will look back and say, 'My goodness, what we did to those poor people. We poisoned them with chemicals and blasted them with radiation.' The apparent cures are truly brutal."

"Yes, I take your point. My friend, who has just died, had all the treatments. They were horribly uncomfortable and the end result was the same. She passed to Spirit World, anyway," said Alice. She then turned to Susie and asked, "How then do you support your students? Bearing in mind that you must be cautious about inflicting your own beliefs on them?"

Susie quoted a few of the stories from her classes, without mentioning any names, of course. One lovely lady had been attending Susie's Thursday evening classes for years. She came with her daughter-in-law. Her husband had died and she greatly missed him, but her family was very good to her, and she had a positive outlook on life. Susie often saw her walking to the shops. She was cheerful and smiley. When she was diagnosed with bowel cancer, this lady firmly put her foot down and said, "I am having no treatment. I will have good days and I will have bad days. But they will be mine." Her family totally supported her decision and knew that, when she died, she did so on her own terms.

As Susie went on to say, "There is one certainty in this life, we all will die. For most people it is not death that frightens them, but rather the manner of their death. If you believe in reincarnation, and if you accept that your spirit goes on, then death can be viewed as a promotion."

At this moment in their conversation, Max burst in announcing that he was 'starving hungry'! Susie waved a goodbye to Alice and bustled in to make dinner.

Later that evening, Susie touched on her discussion with Rob. She had read an article about Soul Midwives and she was very taken with the notion of supporting terminal patients as they passed to Spirit World. Susie had a great friend, who had trained with her, and she offered yoga classes at the local hospital under the banner of the Macmillan nurses. Often she would recommend Susie's classes for those who recovered and wanted to move on to mainstream classes. Susie broached the subject of, perhaps, running a care home for old yogis. Rob was immediately taken with the idea. This could be something that he and his lovely wife could do together, at some time in the future.

Meanwhile, within her own family, Susie was observing old age and its effects. Grandma Doris was going downhill. She was becoming more forgetful and more irritable. Marion was finding that her mother was a full-time job. And not a very rewarding job, at that. She found herself asking Susie to 'cover' occasionally, so that she could have a break. It was almost like setting up a baby-sitter. When she left Susie in charge, her emotions were, at the same time, guilt and relief. She knew that Susie's yoga background would stand her in good stead, and that she would remain patient and loving, despite the provocations. Their dear little cat, Chico, was a wonderful 'carer', spending hours sitting on Doris's knee. Cats are natural yogis and can readily establish a soul-to-soul connection.

One day, Susie suggested to Doris that she might like to try meditation. She explained that it is fine to sit in a chair to meditate, as long as the back is upright. Doris seemed to be fairly open to the idea, so when she was comfortable, with her feet flat on the floor, and Chico asleep on her knee, Susie led her into an awareness of the breath meditation exercise. She simply asked her grandmother to focus on the tip of her nose; then to notice the cool air entering her nostrils; and then to notice the warmer air leaving her nostrils. If any thoughts came into her mind, she would allow them to pass and then return to focussing on the tip of her nose. All went well for a couple of minutes, until Susie noticed that her grandmother's breathing had changed. She had fallen asleep! Ah well, thought Susie, at least we made a start.

Susie's tutor had talked to them about the microcosm and macrocosm, on one occasion. She could now see how this was working in her own life. She was watching her sons growing up, taking some of the yoga teachings into their lives, and also seeing her grandmother slowing down. It was highly possible for her grandmother to take yoga teachings into this new phase of her life, and Susie felt that it was her duty to give her some yoga tools. Within her family, the whole range of the world's age span was present. Her life represented the struggles and the beauty of the world. Susie took this into her meditation one morning. She saw clearly how yoga offered a wide variety of tools to serve all circumstances. It was as though yoga provided everyone with a tool bag of beliefs, practices and techniques, so that in every situation or phase, there was support to be found. It seemed to Susie that being a yoga teacher was at once rewarding, fulfilling, challenging and all-encompassing.

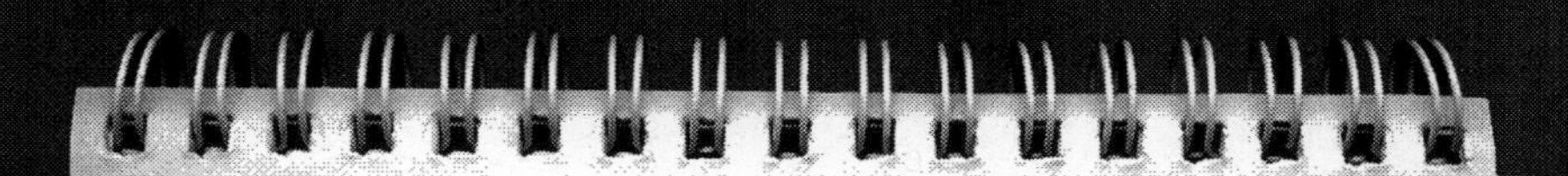

Suggestions from *Yoga Prescribed*

Hatha yoga practice quickly helps breathing problems and most back problems.

Relaxation techniques are the key to releasing stress.

Pranayama exercises clear the mind and improve concentration and stamina.

Children's yoga classes give the young a sound awareness of their bodies, solid self-esteem and tools for dealing with life's challenges.

Mandalas give both children and adults a creative outlet. The choice of colours and shapes can tell a great deal about the psychological state.

Pet therapy is becoming more widely recognised. Years ago a survey endeavoured to discover why some patients recovering from heart attacks did so more fully and quickly than others. The findings were fascinating. It was not down to factors such as whether the patients were married or not, or where they lived, but it was shown that those who owned pets made a more complete and speedy recovery.

(If in doubt about trying new suggestions, check with your doctor or health professional.)

CHAPTER 11

ROB AND A COMPELLING ARGUMENT FOR CIDER VINEGAR

Susie's husband felt enormously supportive towards her yoga classes and beliefs. He had observed the effects of yoga practice on their family and friends. He would, occasionally, turn up to one of her classes. He thoroughly enjoyed Salutation to the Sun and the *Pranayama* techniques such as *Kapalabhati* (the skull-cleansing breath). His own parents had not come across yoga at all until Susie came into their lives, but they were naturally gentle and equable people. He had grown up in a very harmonious home, where laughter was never far from the surface.

Rob had fallen in love with Susie immediately and deeply. During their marriage he had experienced an ever-deepening love and soul connection with her. He liked nothing better than to watch her move, she had a grace that mesmerised him. Seeing her demonstrate the postures in her classes made Rob glow with pride. He mulled over the idea of opening an old yogi's home with Susie as he drove to work one day. Rob was not overly ambitious. He had achieved a good standard of living for his family, but he had seen how stress had destroyed the health and well-being of some of his colleagues. He did not want to follow that route. He considered where the boys were in their education. They were now studying for their G.C.S.E.s and their teachers were predicting a good outcome. He and Susie had every reason to believe that the twins would go to university. Now, that would be the time to make a life change. He felt confident that the two of them would be able to work together and to make a success of a new venture. He put his thoughts on the back burner, as he parked his car and went into the office.

It was several nights later that he and Susie were sitting in the garden having a catch up while the boys were revising in their rooms. Rob explained his thoughts about a joint venture, following on from Susie's suggestion.

"I can bring my skills as a web-designer to the project. I would, of course, be happy to do the practical tasks, such as maintenance of the building, gardening etc. The yoga teaching and meditation would be your department, but what we would need to consider is recruiting someone with nursing skills. I'm thinking after the boys go to university would be the perfect time to launch our plan," Rob said.

Susie grinned broadly. She would love to work with Rob, and she felt strongly that there was a big hole in the way old folk were handled in our society. Yoga would help elderly people to live in the moment and to pursue their spiritual progress. Their strength, suppleness and stamina would all improve with daily yoga practice. Rob firmly believed that when you make a decision, the Universe comes in behind you. This was to prove the case.

Meanwhile, there were one or two changes that Rob could effect in his own life. He made a point of attending weekly classes with Susie. He observed some of the older yogis and how they adapted their practice. He read extensively about how yoga affects longevity. He and Susie began to play with ideas on the name of their old yogis' home, and pondered as to whether it would be more politically correct to describe it as 'an elderly yogi's home' instead!

Rob's own grandmother took cider vinegar and honey each day, he remembered. She looked frail and genteel but she had a robust attitude to life. She was the first to state that we are responsible for our own health and, unlike others in her generation, resisted visiting the doctor. She was convinced that cider vinegar mixed with honey kept her joints in good order and kept arthritis at bay. She also used the vinegar on bites and stings, and as a gargle diluted with water. Rob could recall her taking kelp tablets daily but could not remember why. He must ask his mother the next time he saw her.

A plan had begun in the couple's minds, but most important now was keeping the household running smoothly as their sons faced their important exams. Two teenagers studying hard created some tension in their normally equable home! Rob was only too happy to help with homework, where he could, and to take the boys out for a pizza when it all got too much.

Meanwhile, Susie determined to talk to her mother, her grandmother and her special neighbours, Ted and Alice about their project. Brainstorming with loved ones was always a good practice.

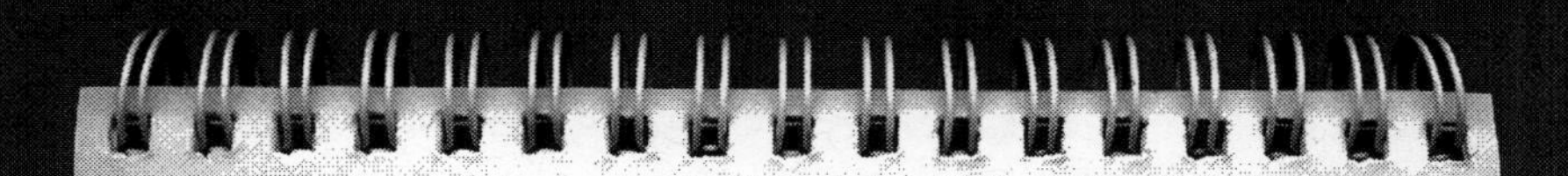

Suggestions from *Yoga Prescribed*

Cider vinegar is an old-fashioned remedy which is beloved by many. It is a panacea, being used in conjunction with honey to keep joints healthy, but also in many other ways. (Do remember to always use a wooden implement in honey and never metal, which interferes with its efficacy.) It is a most useful gargle, helping to alleviate sore throats and infections. It is a natural disinfectant so is very helpful for clearing tummy bugs. Cider vinegar can be used on insect bites and nettle stings. It clears fungal infections and acne.

(All suggestions are made with the best possible motives. These ideas may help you when used in support of medical advice.)

CHAPTER 12

JIM'S DEAR FACE

Susie had continued her meditation routine with Joanne. Even though Joanne's son, Jack, had arrived home safely, they still worked as a partnership. It was early one morning, when Susie was meditating in her favourite quiet corner, that she received a vision. She lost awareness of herself and she could feel a different energy. Then a larger-than-life image of her father entered her space. His face was the dear face she knew and loved, but he was dressed in monk's robes. His voice was so loud and resonant that, for a brief moment, she was worried that he would wake the twins.

"We are not apart," he boomed. "We are always together. We are one. You have no need to look for me because I am here. We connect all the time, on many different levels, but we are always one. Do not fret. Do not search. Feel no separation. Trust in your process, as I trust in mine. The love we share is all enduring. Be happy. Follow your path. Do your duty. We will meet again, but not in this lifetime. And that is fine. All is well, and all shall be well. You are my dearest daughter and the love I feel for you is eternal." With that, Jim's face smiled and was so full of love and peace that Susie's heart sang. Then his image disappeared, and once more Susie was aware of her surroundings and her meditation shawl resting on her shoulders.

A deep peace settled on Susie's mind. She felt totally reassured and she felt totally loved. Her acceptance was complete. She knew that she had been in the presence of her father's energy and that she could release her search. She squirrelled away her father's face and his words in that part of her heart that belonged just to him. This was the part that had ached for so long, but now no more. All was well, and all shall be well. As Susie moved about the kitchen, preparing breakfast for her husband and her sons, she felt complete.

Susie hugged her vision to her for that day, not quite wanting to break the spell by sharing it. That night in bed, though, as she cuddled close to Rob, he asked, "Are you working with *Santosha* (contentment) this week in class? You feel so deeply content." Susie giggled. She should have known that Rob would pick up on the change! Softly, she told him about her vision, and he held her even closer as the full impact of the occurrence settled in his mind. He had only met Jim briefly, before he disappeared forever from their lives, but he fully recognised how important her father was to his lovely wife. He could not be happier that she had been given a message.

Joanne and Susie met for a walk and a talk the next day. Joanne brought her poodle, also called Jim, and he had a wonderful romp in the country park, meeting up with new doggy friends. Joanne was thrilled with Susie's news – a little mystified perhaps, but definitely thrilled. She wanted to know if they should move their meditation focus in another direction, and Susie considered this for several moments before replying. They had managed a total success rate from their venture. Joanne's son, Jack, had 'seen' a vision of his mother and had made the decision to return home. Susie's father, Jim, had known that Susie was seeking him and had sent a powerful message in response. The joint meditation was a powerful tool. It was not one to be abandoned without careful thought. Could they move from the particular to the general? Susie suggested that they continue to meditate at the same time as one another and simply dedicate the practice to all those souls who felt lost at this time. They could dedicate their joint practice to the angel called Rochel. It is she who finds lost things. Susie felt that more thought needed to go into how they would proceed from here but, like Joanne, she was reluctant to lose their impetus.

Susie considered whether to tell her mother what had happened during her meditation. She decided to wait for the right moment. Meanwhile, Rob was partially right; Susie had indeed moved on from theming her classes on the first limb of yoga, the *Yamas*, to the second limb of yoga, the *Niyamas*. The Yamas are self-restraints: *Ahimsa*, non-violence; *Satya*, truthfulness; *Asteya*, non-stealing; *Brahmacharya*, awareness of forces beyond ourselves; and *Aparigraha*, non-greed. They are known as the 'Don'ts'. The Niyamas are the observances: *Saucha*, purity or cleanliness; *Santosha*, contentment; *Tapas*, self-discipline; *Swadhyaya*, spiritual study; *Ishvara Pranidana*, surrender. These are known as the 'Do's'. Susie had a neat way of introducing a theme and then drip-feeding its meaning as the class progressed. She thought of it as planting seeds. In this way she hoped that the ancient messages of yoga philosophy would grow and spread. That week they were looking at Aparigraha, non-greed. She remembered reading that Gandhi had said: 'There is enough for everyone's need, but not enough for everyone's greed.'

Susie had a new student called Margaret, who was suffering with carpal tunnel syndrome. It was very painful and practising poses such as the cat or downward-facing dog were impossible. Susie did some research to see if there were any natural aids for this condition. Some folk had received relief by visiting a cranial osteopath, or a physiotherapist who was skilled in sports remedial massage. It could apparently be caused by a trapped nerve in the neck. Certain herbs had also proved most helpful: cumin, turmeric, cayenne, chamomile and rubbing in comfrey ointment. Susie passed on these suggestions to Margaret, who said that she and her husband loved curries and so would definitely be eating more of the anti-inflammatories, turmeric and cumin.

Each yoga class gave opportunities for the sharing of information. Susie remembered her tutor saying that a yoga teacher learns much more from her students than her teachers! It occurred to Susie that, on some level, her father had witnessed her spiritual growth as a yoga teacher. He had stated that he was following his right path, and she derived enormous comfort from that. He had also stated that they would not meet up in this lifetime, which clearly meant that he believed in karma and life after death. Susie knew in her heart of hearts that they would one day meet, on a different plane perhaps, and that was good enough.

Susie called in to see her mother and her grandmother on the way back home from her morning class. Doris was asleep in the chair, while Marion was on the computer. Immediately, the kettle was put on, and Marion was very glad to have a catch up with her daughter. Marion was looking tired and she confessed that looking after Doris was exhausting. They discussed asking for help, perhaps it would be possible for someone to come in and sit with Doris occasionally. She had become so forgetful that Marion worried about her putting something on the stove and then forgetting. She was concerned that a fire was a strong possibility.

The whole cycle of life fascinated Susie. Her boys were growing up, her grandmother was sliding down. Susie had her own belief system and felt that she had a pretty good hold on the meaning of life. She fully embraced the idea of not looking back in anger, nor forward in fear, but around you in awareness. She pottered around in the garden for an hour before the boys came home from school. Touching the earth was always therapeutic, and Susie remembered, with affection, seeing her father mow the lawn. He was most peaceful when he was working with his hands.

She found that her memories had a different quality to them now. The familiar ache had completely left her. She felt that Jim was safe, was following his path and was finding the meaning to his own life. Perhaps, on some level, he was clearing the path ahead for her. She found herself speaking to her father in her mind and it felt quite natural. She glanced over the fence at Alice and Ted's beautifully ordered garden. They were getting older, too, but were still very active. Their positive attitude to life, and to living each day fully, was an inspiration to everyone. Susie determined to tell Alice about her vision very soon.

Later that evening, on an impulse, Susie phoned her mother and asked for a photograph of the three of them, when Susie was a new baby. This would set off a chain of memories for Marion, which was to prove cleansing and healing. Marion selected a beautiful print and busied herself into town, the next day, to choose a photo frame that would do it justice. Eventually, she settled on a stylish wooden one, which she knew would have pleased Jim's craftsman's eye. She knew nothing of Susie's vision yet, but she was a forgiving soul and was glad to let go of the past. She remembered reading somewhere that forgiveness does not alter the past but it does change the future. She no longer felt a connection with Jim, but she was endlessly proud of the daughter who they had made together.

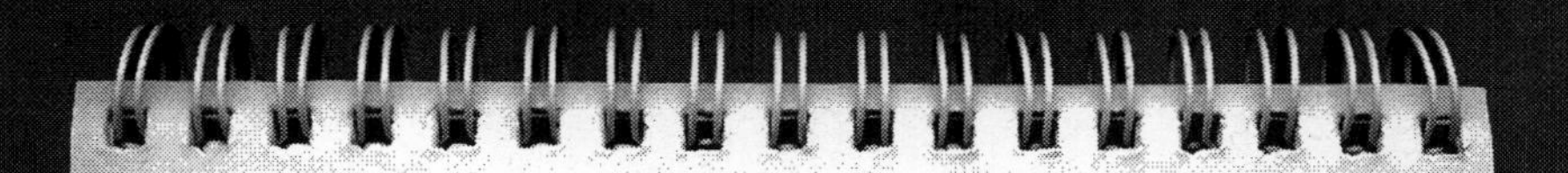

Suggestions from *Yoga Prescribed*

Consulting with a cranial osteopath or a sports remedial masseur can be helpful in alleviating carpal tunnel syndrome. It is also useful to include natural anti-inflammatories such as turmeric in the diet.

(All suggestions are based on anecdotal evidence. See your doctor if in doubt.)

CHAPTER 13

ALICE ON DYING

"Ted and I have been talking about dying. Is that morbid?" Alice asked Susie one evening, as they sat in the garden, drinking chamomile tea.

"Not at all" replied Susie. "That is the one certainty that we all have in life, that one day we will die."

"I'm glad you feel like that, Susie. I know that if I was to die right now, at this very moment, that I would have lived a good life. I'm surrounded by love. Ted has been a wonderful companion. We have two beautiful children, and they have made their own families and their own lives. We have the best neighbours in the world too!" (Here she grinned at Susie and giggled.) "We've created a home and a life for ourselves that reflects who we are and it seems to me that we have been blessed."

"Yes, you have been blessed," Susie agreed, "but by your natures you draw good things to you. You are both so positive and upbeat. That attitude is contagious. People feel more optimistic when they are around you. We all want to be part of your loving circle!"

"I suppose," continued Alice "that most people do not fear their death as much as their manner of dying. In a perfect passing to Spirit World, I would choose to die peacefully in my sleep, as

Ted would, too. No commotion, no drama, just a quiet slipping away. And I would not want to leave anyone upset or mourning. I want all my special people to know just how much I loved them."

"Mm. I'm pretty sure that you can guarantee that, Alice. All joking aside, we feel entirely privileged to have lived next door to you for all these years. You and Ted are part of our family; a very special chosen part. Rob and I have been talking about perhaps opening an 'old yogis' home.' We both love the idea of giving older folk meaning, contentment and spirituality in their last months or years. We feel that death is not discussed in our society. Everyone avoids the subject, as though, in some way, that will protect us from the inevitable."

Alice nodded her head. "Nature teaches us the way. The garden wakes up in the spring, and suddenly we notice colour, and the birds singing. Then comes the summer, when everything is in abundance and there's a lot of work to be done. Autumn follows, yielding its fruits and allowing everything to begin the dying down process. And then here comes winter again, when apparently the garden is dead but actually it is just dormant. Life is like that. The love that Ted and I have experienced in our lives may appear to have gone with our passing, but actually it is still there, below the surface. I believe that no love is wasted. The energy, creativity and love that we have put out will never be lost."

"You're so wise, dear Alice," Susie replied, reaching over to give her a hug. "Promise me that you will come and visit me from Spirit World, when you can get away, and keep me on the straight and narrow!"

"I certainly shall, and I'll be there to welcome your old yogis, as well, when they get promotion and join us above!"

Susie marvelled at the fact, as she prepared for bed that night, that her very best friend was from a completely different generation. She hoped that when she was Alice's age she would spend time with young people.

The Friday class had been talking about nutrition. Susie had mentioned the three *Gunas*, which are the energies that combine to make the Universe. The *Rajasic* energy is restless and active; the *Tamasic* energy is dull and lethargic; the *Sattvic* energy is balanced and calm. Susie had told them that different foods brought about these energies in the body. Although we need all three energies, we need them to be in a good balance. Yogis choose foods that will encourage the Sattvic energy. '*The foods which increase life, purity, strength, health, joy and cheerfulness, which are savoury and oleaginous, substantial and agreeable, are dear to the Sattvic people.*' (This quote is from the Bhagavad Gita, Chapter 17 Verse 8.) Sattvic foods are such as fresh organic vegetables, fresh fruit, pure filtered water. Rajasic food is hot and spicy. Coffee, tea, tobacco and stimulants of all kinds fall into this category. '*Foods that are bitter, sour, saline, excessively hot, pungent, dry and burning, are liked by the Rajasic and are productive of pain, grief and disease.*' (Bhagavad Gita, Chapter 17 Verse 9.) Tamasic food is stale and over-cooked; it includes processed foods, and meals that have been reheated. '*That food which is stale, tasteless, putrid, rotten and impure refuse, is the food liked by the Tamasic.*' (Gita Chapter 17 Verse 10.) The manner of eating is also relevant to the Gunas. For example, Rajasic people tend to 'eat on the go' or stand up to eat or eat while working. There is a very interesting quote from the Taittriya Upanishad which says: '*From food all beings are born. Having been born, they grow by food. Food is eaten by all beings and it also eats them.*' As Susie remarked to her Friday class, "Now that is food for thought!"

Most yogis are vegetarians and they discover, as they work more and more with cleansing their bodies and fuelling them with prana, (the life-force, life-giving energy) that Rajasic and

Tamasic foods give *them* up. It is evolutionary. Over the years, Susie's awareness of her body and what best suited it, had developed into a constant stream of communication. That is not to say that she would begrudge herself the occasional ice-cream! What could be nicer than sitting on a wall with the family, looking out to sea, and licking a delicious cone! She balanced this, though, with big helpings of superfoods in the week's meals; foods such as oats, yogurt, broccoli, pineapple, tomatoes, spinach, parsley and watercress. Both the boys loved porridge and also oatcakes, which contain slow release carbohydrates. Broccoli is a great source of iron, vitamin C and beta-carotene. It is said that broccoli might even regulate insulin! Pineapple acts as an anti-inflammatory, as does turmeric. Tomatoes are a powerful antioxidant and spinach may help reduce the risk of cataracts. It is also rich in iron, as is watercress. Susie was a big fan of ginger, which is so helpful for the digestive system. Ayurvedic medicine fascinated her. It combines with yoga to offer a complete health system.

Ted and Alice had always eaten a nutritious diet, so Susie and Rob were hopeful that they had many years to live. Yet her discussion with Alice about dying had brought an idea to her mind. Next time they had some free time, she would suggest that Alice and Ted should plan their own funerals. She and Rob were on hand to make sure that their wishes were carried out to the letter, and one thing was for sure, there would be muffled bells for Ted! Susie wondered if her grandmother, Doris, had planned her funeral. She was keeping Marion busy. She had been regularly waking her up at two in the morning, to tell her it was time to go shopping!

Rob came home with excellent news that week. He had been promoted, and his salary had gone up in consequence. He set up a saving plan towards their future plans of opening an old yogis' home. Susie's classes were all well supported and the couple were on a good financial footing. They were very aware, though, that it would not be long till Max and Toby would be off to university. That would be a drain on their resources, but a happy one!

The discussion on nutrition continued at the next week's classes. Joanne had been researching cider vinegar. Most people were aware that cider vinegar and honey is a wonderful treatment for arthritis, and many people use cider vinegar neat on bites and nettle stings. Fewer realise that it is a natural disinfectant, clearing tummy bugs and even dissolving kidney stones. It regulates the pH balance in the body and relieves nausea and heartburn; it helps to relieve asthma and allergies; it lowers glucose levels in diabetes and helps weight loss by curbing appetite and breaking down fat; it also relieves gout, migraines and sinus infections; it lowers the blood pressure and cholesterol; it reduces inflammation, conditions and detangles hair; it gets rid of nail fungus, and fungal and bacterial rashes; cider vinegar helps reduce and prevent acne, and gets rid of warts. The classes all agreed that every home should have a bottle!

Joanne, delighted with the interest in her research, went home to investigate sweet potatoes. They had long been a favourite in her household, and she knew that they were packed with antioxidants like beta-carotene, and with vitamins C, E and D. She was soon to discover that they are also rich in minerals such as manganese and iron, and they are high in potassium, which helps to lower blood pressure.

Each of Susie's classes was alive with interesting characters, all of whom had their own stories to tell, their own conditions and their own reasons for coming to yoga. Many friendships were formed and information was shared. Some of Susie's more spiritual students had noticed a shift in her recently. Ever since her father had 'visited' her and given her his message, she had manifested a deeper inner strength. It was as though her masculine side had become more evident. Susie had always been pretty, feminine and supple, but now she was looking really strong in the powerful postures. The two sides of her being were combining in a different and fascinating way. This coincided with Susie feeling the energy of a new spirit guide and, although she did not share this information with her students, the change manifested itself through her teaching.

Life continued pleasantly. The twins were studying hard and talking more about universities. Susie's classes were growing in size and she so loved teaching them. As she grew and developed her own style, more unusual students were drawn to her.

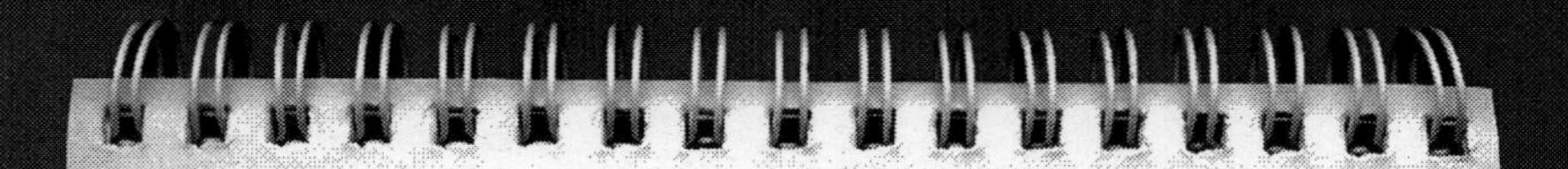

Suggestions from *Yoga Prescribed*

Study the Gunas to understand the three energies that make up the Universe. Insights are gained in reference to diet, too.

Cider vinegar, mentioned before, is a panacea.

There is an old Chinese proverb that states that 'Food is medicine'. Sweet potatoes are an excellent addition to the diet.

(All suggestions are based on anecdotal evidence and yoga research.)

CHAPTER 14

ROB, SUSIE AND THE BUSINESS PLAN

Everything changed all at once. The boys attained the 'A' level results that they needed, and were accepted by their chosen universities. Max was thrilled to get into Oxford and Toby was equally ecstatic to get into Durham. Toby's course offered a year in a University abroad, and he had his sights set on Boston, U.S.A.

The end of summer was busy with getting the boys everything they needed and, all too soon, they were off. Susie dreaded the 'goodbyes'. This was the first time that the twins had been separated from one another, and the first time Rob and Susie had parted with the boys for anything longer than a week. She was determined not to embarrass the boys by crying, when they parted, but it took all her willpower to save the tears for the car on the journey homeward. The more she bawled, the more pink around the edges Rob became!

Susie was still mourning the absence of her noisy sons (who had settled well and were really loving university life) when dear Ted had a massive heart attack and died. He was just outside the greenhouse when he collapsed, and Alice saw him fold over as she was washing up at the kitchen sink. She was beside him in a moment, but she knew he was already dead. She said her fond goodbyes to the man she had loved nearly all her life, held him close, and then went to phone the ambulance. She was to say later that this was the perfect way for Ted to pass to Spirit World. He was in his beloved garden and he was still active. How he would have hated to be restricted to a wheelchair, or worse, to have been bed-bound.

Susie, already really emotional, broke down and wept for hours when she heard the news. As she hugged Alice close, it was a moot point as to who was comforting who. Alice's family came from Watford and Australia, and together they gave Ted a wonderful send-off. The church bells were muffled out of respect for a very special man, and a stalwart of the ringing world. Alice insisted that the twins were not to return for the funeral, saying that they had given Ted enormous pleasure during his life and he would want them now to immerse themselves in their studies and their new lives.

Susie kept a close eye on Alice in the next few weeks. The sparkle had gone from her eyes and she seemed to move more slowly, but she was coping with her daily tasks. Rob did his best to keep her garden neat and to harvest Ted's fruit and vegetables. They often invited her in for meals and talked of Ted. On one such occasion, Alice amazed them by recounting a conversation that she had had with Ted the week before he died. They had been talking about Rob and Susie's plan to open a home for elderly yogis. Ted was most taken with the idea, and he'd suggested to Alice that they could donate their cottage as part of the establishment. That would mean that Rob and Susie would own the three cottages and they would be able to configure a reasonable-sized property. In return, Ted and Alice could be inmates for life. Alice had thought long and hard about this idea, since Ted had died, and she dearly wanted to bring it to fruition. She had discussed it with her children, Rosemary and James. They both immediately agreed that they did not need the money from their parents' cottage, and they said they would be delighted to know that Alice would be looked after forever. They had tremendous respect and affection for Rob and Susie, and they knew that their mother could not have been in more caring hands. So it was agreed, Alice would bequeath her pretty home to them in return for living out her days as their very first resident. She was just the right person to fit into a community of yogis. She understood the philosophies, had observed yoga as a way of life amongst her young neighbours, and was open to learning new ways to move her body.

It felt to Susie that the Universe had come in behind them and that all the stars were aligning to move their project forward. She and Rob began to explore ideas for extending the premises so that they could build on a yoga hall. They approached the local planning office with their thoughts. To their delight there did not seem to be any major obstacles to their scheme.

Alice got busy de-cluttering, and this focussed her mind. She was deeply content to be helping with a project that was so very worthwhile. Her mind was fixed on bringing into reality a scheme that Ted had approved at the end of his life. Rob was careful to include her in all the plans for the changes, and he was excited to be taking on the role of project manager. Just as he was beginning to wonder how he was going to find the time to do a full-time job and to organise the build, he was offered a job share at work. The timing was impeccable. He selected to work on Wednesday afternoon, and all day Thursday and Friday. This would dovetail beautifully with Susie's classes. Her yoga week was heavier at the beginning of the week. She had three classes on Mondays, two on Tuesdays, Wednesdays, Thursdays, and one on a Friday. When the home was in full swing, there would always be one of them available. Rob could now cover her Wednesday morning practice, and he would be home in time for her Wednesday evening class and her two evening classes on a Thursday night. Susie decided to amalgamate her Friday morning class with the Wednesday morning one, and that way she had a full day on Friday to devote to the residents of the home. It was all coming together!

Rob began writing a business plan. He anticipated that they would need ten residents to make the business viable. His concern was how to organise the building, even with the extension, so that they had living accommodation for themselves, and also for their sons when they were on holiday from university. He and Susie talked long into the night and explored options. They began to wonder if they could rent a small place in the village, but how they were going to finance the whole project was becoming a deep concern.

Just when everyone was feeling a little stressed, Susie's grandmother tripped in the back garden and fell heavily, breaking her hip. Marion called the ambulance, and Doris was taken off to the local hospital. She kept protesting that she did not want a fuss but she was clearly disoriented. Marion did not feel that she could leave her mother, so she called Susie. She asked her to feed Chico, their ginger cat, and to make sure that the back door was locked. They had left in such a rush that she was unsure what had been done and what had not.

Susie did as her mother asked, then she called into the supermarket to buy roses for Doris. She planned to visit her the next afternoon and she knew that yellow roses were her favourite flowers. Her mother kept her informed with texts about Doris's treatment. She had undergone an operation for a replacement hip. Marion was not at all sure that she was sturdy enough for the procedure, but the surgeon had recommended it.

She did not rally after the operation quite as they would have liked, and by the time Susie saw her grandmother, she was looking very poorly indeed. She immediately volunteered to stay the night at her bedside while her mother went home to get some sleep, but Marion would not hear of it. So Susie and Rob shifted their attention away from their business plans to worrying about Marion and Doris.

The next morning, Rob phoned into work to explain that he would be late, and then he visited Doris with his anxious wife. She had spent a fitful night and had developed a nasty cough. The nurses were checking her frequently and Marion's blurry eyes showed her concern. Susie and Rob took Doris's hands and sat with her, talking gently about the twins, about Chico, and about the garden, while Marion went to freshen up and have a cup of coffee. Doris was confused, certainly, but she knew them and she squeezed their hands. When, after Marion had returned, they took their leave, Doris managed a feeble wave and muttered, "Give my love to the boys. Don't worry them. I don't want a fuss." After that, her troublesome cough began and her full attention was demanded to cope with it.

By the following morning, she had died from pneumonia. They were all in shock. First of all the twins had gone away to university, which was as it should be but was stressful. Then their wonderful neighbour, Ted, had died suddenly. And now they must part with their beloved grandmother. It felt like a very cruel blow and, once again, Rob stepped up to the plate for his wife and his mother-in-law. He had broad shoulders and he needed them. His was the shoulder that they cried on. Much sooner than they could have anticipated, they were organising another funeral, and the village bells were muffled again. This time Max and Toby did come home, already looking more confident and worldly. They were smart young men in their dark suits. They both read a piece in the church. Marion cried to think of how much her mother would have loved that.

So everything changed all at once, as sometimes happens in life. It is as though folk bumble along on a plateau for a while and then the Universe decrees that some lessons are overdue. Marion dreaded going back to her huge, rambling house, where her parents had lived so happily. Even though her mother had become trying and confused lately, she would miss her desperately. It was her mother's support that she had sought in her difficult marriage with Jim; it was to her mother that she returned when Jim disappeared; it was with her mother that she shared her day-to-day life. Chico missed Doris, too. He had been her companion and had spent long hours on her lap in the conservatory, and on the bottom of her bed. Marion and Chico rattled around in the old, sprawling house for a while, comforting one another.

Susie and Rob were still debating the business plan for their elderly yogi's home. They talked to Marion about it, as much to distract her as anything else. She understood the dilemma. How did they arrange the accommodation so that they had a home, too? As she sat in their pretty lounge, with their cat, Pat, squeezed on the chair beside her, an idea began to play in her mind. She decided to say nothing until she had done some research.

The very next day, Marion phoned the estate agent and had her mother's house valued. It sat in a very lovely one-acre garden, and it had beautiful views of the hills. The estate agent was impressed and, although he recognised that it needed some updating, he gave Marion a favourable valuation. She was to inherit everything from her mother's will, and probate should therefore be quite straightforward. Marion determined to put the house on the market as soon as ever she could. Meanwhile, she asked if she could come over on Friday evening, for a chat, and could Susie invite Alice, too?

So they all gathered in Susie's lounge and, after hugs and elderflower cordial, Marion dominated the conversation. She explained that she had been thinking hard about the family accommodation, both during the building of the extension and afterwards when the home was up and running. She suggested that Rob and Susie evacuated their house and moved in with her.

"Mum's house is plenty big enough for all of us, and I would like to invite Alice as well. You can't stay here, Alice, with all the noise and chaos, and Mum would have loved to think of you in her old room." Susie went to give her mother a hug, but Marion said, "I haven't finished my proposal yet! That would be our short-term solution, while the build is taking place, and the only challenge I foresee with that is introducing your cat, Pat, to Chico!" At this they all laughed. "But long-term we need to consider selling Mum's house, and buying a place for all of us in this village. Although Mum's house is only a short way away, it is too far. We need to be on hand. And I say 'we' advisedly, because I would very much like to be part of this project. I would be delighted to do the bookkeeping, and to help out where needed. I have some amateur experience as far as taking care of the elderly goes, after my time with my own parents. We can organise it so that one of the three of us, that is Susie, Rob and me, is always available at the home but, for pure convenience, we need to find a home close by."

Everyone began to talk at once. This was a brilliant solution. Alice was very pleased to think of moving in with Marion. Much as she respected Rob's abilities as project manager, she had a sneaking suspicion that the build would take longer than they hoped, and that it would be a noisy and dirty affair. She would be very happy to return when all was pristine, and to take up her rightful place as the number one resident.

Rob shifted into top gear. He contacted a friend of his who was an architect and they had several meetings. Their plan was to put a two-storey extension on the back of the three cottages. The ground floor would be the yoga hall, and above there would be four en-suite bedrooms. They decided that they needed ten en-suite bedrooms, in all, and two bathrooms downstairs. The kitchen would need to be extended to meet the catering needs, and they would also need a good-sized dining room. The finished plans were excellent, and everyone was in suspense when they were submitted to the Planning Office. With a few minor changes the plans were approved and they were off! The architect recommended a local builder. Fortunately Rob's savings would cover the first part of the build.

Meanwhile, Marion had been busy at her end. She had cleared Doris's bedroom and spring-cleaned it. Alice would be very comfortable there. She prepared the spare bedroom for Rob and Susie. Then she explained to Chico that he would need to be a very generous cat, as he would soon be sharing his home with another feline. Pat was, by now, an elderly gentleman, but still easy-going. Marion got busy in the garden, with the thought that it would not be long till the house would be on the market. It felt good to have plans and to feel useful.

Susie was elated. That her long-held dream was coming to fruition and that her family and dear friend would all be involved was amazing. She themed her class that week on synchronicity and explained how so-called coincidences rarely are just that. Sometimes you think of someone that you have not seen for years and then the phone rings and it is them. Or a memory pops into your mind and someone else mentions it. Some mornings you wake up and just know that everything will suddenly fall into place. Susie firmly believed that once you make a plan, the Universe comes in behind you and makes all conditions favourable for that plan to come to fruition. She chose this reading that particular week, which is often wrongly attributed to Johann Wolfgang von Goethe (although the last three sentences belong to him). In fact it was W.H. Murray in 'The Scottish Himalayan Expedition, 1951', who wrote:

Begin it now

Until one is committed, there is hesitancy, the chance to draw back, always ineffectiveness. Concerning all acts of initiative (and creation), there is one elementary truth, the ignorance of which kills countless ideas and splendid plans: that the moment one definitely commits oneself, then Providence moves too. All sorts of things occur to help one that would never otherwise have occurred. A whole stream of events issues from the decision, raising in one's favour all manner of unforeseen incidents and meetings and material assistance which no man could have dreamed would have come his way. Whatever you can do or dream you can, begin it. Boldness has genius, power and magic in it. Begin it now.

It was while she was teaching her Wednesday class that another idea flashed into her mind. She would ask Joanne if she would like to train as a nutritionist. It would be enormously helpful to have an expert on board who could research the dietary needs of all the residents of the home. She and Joanne had become so close over the time when they meditated together. The return of Joanne's son, Jack, had been a day of celebration for them both.

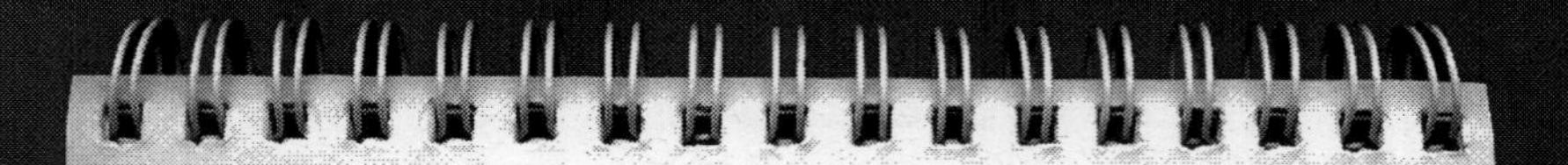

Suggestions from *Yoga Prescribed*

Look for synchronicity in your life. When making a decision, trust that the Universe will support you.

CHAPTER 15

FRIENDS, CONTACTS AND METTA

Susie, Rob and Alice had moved in with Marion. Life soon settled into a rhythm with Marion and Alice enjoying one another's company during the day and doing the housework together. Rob and Susie came in and out for meals and sleep. They were both incredibly busy, what with work and overseeing the build. In any spare time available, Rob was creating a website so that as soon as the premises were completed he could begin recruiting for elderly yogis. Susie recognised that her friends and contacts would be invaluable in spreading the word. She contacted her tutor, who was always delighted to hear from her. She came on board with enormous enthusiasm, even offering her beautiful, furry dog for pet therapy visits. She would be happy to contact all of her graduated teachers and to share brochures with her students. Susie felt supported on all fronts.

Joanne, who had been enjoying sharing information on food with Susie's class, readily agreed to train as a nutritionist. She was flattered to be asked and knew that she would be able to work with her good friend. She had also offered to help with the soft furnishings, when the time came, as her background was in design.

Rob was experiencing some frustration. The weather had held back some of the work, and practical decisions sometimes had to be made quickly, with little time for research. He was concerned about the budget. They had needed to put a lot of their furniture into storage, which had to be factored into their expenses. One day, as he chewed the fat with the builder, the idea flashed through his mind that his father-in-law, Jim, would have been an excellent advisor. He had only known Jim for a very short time but he recognised his skills as a craftsman. Susie, though, had inherited his 'eye' and was remarkably intuitive in blending style with practicality. This project was yet another test of their relationship. They took it in turns to bolster one another, so that when frustrations built they always had a sounding-board. Their enthusiasm did not wane, but sometimes their energies were low.

Marion put her house on the market. She reckoned that she and Alice could keep it neat enough for viewings, despite the fact that it was somewhat full. She hoped to get a buyer before the twins came home on holiday from university. Then the house would be straining at the seams! Her estate agent was obliging, and charming. He admired Marion and her positive attitude to life. He was optimistic about finding the right purchaser.

Susie planned a class on Metta, which is universal, unselfish, all-embracing love. For her, it was the anchor of yoga philosophy. She felt total unconditional love towards her weekly students, and she intended to run the elderly yogis' home on the same principle. It was going to be an interesting experiment. It would be a test of her beliefs and how well she actually lived her yoga. Working with residents like Alice would not test her, but others may be more cantankerous!

The estate agent, Phil, had brought a steady stream of potential buyers to view Marion's house. One couple were very interested. They had just sold their own house in Hertfordshire, and they were looking for a place where they would be nearer to their daughter and her family. The garden would be perfect for their two retriever dogs, and there were lovely walks for them to explore nearby. Marion and Alice had their fingers crossed.

Meanwhile, Phil had suggested that they look at a couple of semi-detached houses that had both just come on to his books. They were just up the road from Susie and Rob's build. They might offer them the type of accommodation that they needed. One house had been modernised quite well, and Phil suggested that Marion could be very comfortable there. The other one was liveable but would need work at some point. Rob could treat that as a project, when he had the time and when the business was up and running. The houses were close enough that they could be summoned quickly, if they were needed at the home. It might just work.

Suddenly, the build was taking shape. At the point when the foundations were being laid, it was just a horrible muddy mess. Ted would have been horrified to see his garden being flattened! But now they were almost at the point of putting in the windows, and Rob was researching bathroom fittings. They were aware that everything had to be user-friendly. Even folk practising yoga might have stiff joints in old age!

Susie came home one day, after two classes, and having done some shopping on the way back. She collapsed gratefully into a chair. Marion got busy and made her a lemon and ginger tea. She did not notice, for a few moments, that both her mother and Alice were grinning broadly.

"Okay. What's going on?" Susie laughed.

"That nice couple have bought the house! We did a bit of haggling, but we've agreed a price and, since they are cash buyers, it should go through quite smoothly!"

Susie was thrilled. She felt a wave of gratitude towards the Universe, towards the nice couple and, of course, towards the estate agent. Marion and Alice had planned a special meal for that night to celebrate, with Alice's famous old-fashioned trifle for dessert. Rob came home to find three women grinning at him!

After their delicious meal, they went to look at the outside of the two semis that Phil had mentioned to them. They were literally a two-minute walk from the home. The one on the left looked loved. It had roses growing around an arch over the gate. Marion was quite taken with it. The other one certainly needed some attention, but it did have a garage and some additional parking space. Rob declared that it had potential and, whilst all his time and energy was at the moment devoted to the build, he could imagine himself developing this home sometime in the future. Perhaps the twins would be up for some physical work in their summer holidays. Rob's concern was how they could possibly pay Marion back. Until the home was up and running, all their money was going in that direction. Marion's attitude was very much about going with the flow. After all, if Alice could hand over her property without a second thought, surely she could finance her daughter and son-in-law's family home. There would be time enough for them to repay her, with their time, their money, and with their support.

They went back home and checked out the properties online. Then they agreed to leave it to Marion to negotiate with the two owners, after she had looked around the houses. If she was happy with them, they would completely trust her judgement. What a lot they had to tell Max and Toby, when they saw them.

So it was that, before many weeks had passed, the build was completed. The three cottages had been converted into an airy, spacious and comfortable residence for ten aging yogis. The yoga hall was beautiful, looking out on to the garden and the trees beyond, and sporting underfloor heating. Rob and his Dad had converted Ted's summerhouse into a meditation hut, and intended to plant a peaceful garden beside it. Alice would help to choose plants that promoted calm and tranquillity, whilst the rest of the garden would be planted out with more vibrant colours. Susie had rung her crystal bell in all the corners of the house to calm the energies. She had played the Gregorian chants in the yoga hall and placed her Tibetan singing bowl in the meditation hut. Time and practise would build on the ambience of both venues.

The front of the house would show the name of the home, and there was now plenty of parking for visitors there. Alice had chosen the room that she wanted, which, to no-one's surprise, was on the side of the property that used to belong to her and to Ted. She arranged her chair so that she could best see the meditation hut, set against the trees. And she looked forward to being part of this new community, which her lovely friends were creating.

Susie gathered everyone in for an evening of planning. Joanne came with her husband, Mark, and Rob looked more relaxed than he had for a while. The website was ready to be launched, at the touch of a button. They had already had three enquiries from folk in the yoga classes. Susie felt her energies rise at the thought that yoga would be prescribed for the residents of the home. She intended to design practices that would promote longevity, health and a sense of well-being in the aging. Her creative juices flowed at the thought of the wonderful challenges ahead. Each yogi would have a daily yoga practice prescribed for them, and they would also partake in the community classes, discussions and nutrition programmes. Their individual dietary needs would be taken into consideration when their food was 'prescribed'.

The next day, a Saturday, Rob and Susie stood in the back garden of their excellent new business, and Rob wrapped his arms around his beautiful wife. As she leant into him, he said, "Well, Darling, we've come a long way together, and we've learned a lot of lessons, but I have a sneaking feeling that our lives are only just now beginning. And that just fills me with the warmest glow."

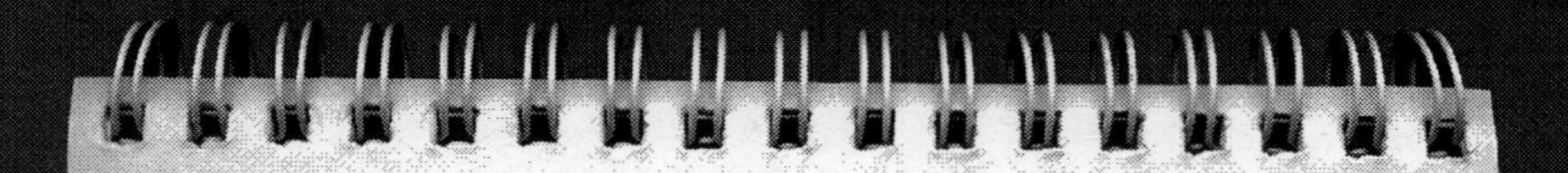

Suggestions from *Yoga Prescribed*

Ringing a bell in the corners of a room dispels negativity. Clapping the hands has the same effect. The Gregorian chants, or New Age music, can be played even when no-one is present. This will calm the energies of a place and is a really helpful practice after spring-cleaning.

Tibetan singing bowls have a profoundly spiritual effect on both spaces and beings.

THE END

Watch out for the sequel – the adventures of the elderly, eccentric and ever amusing folk in the 'Yoga Home'.